INTENTIONAL COMMUNITY IN BRITAIN
12th Edition

Edited by
Chris Coates
James Dennis
Jonathan How
Kirsten Stevens-Wood

DIGGERS AND DREAMERS PUBLICATIONS

Diggers & Dreamers
Publications
2021

First published
2021
D&D Publications
BCM Edge
London
WC1N 3XX

ISBN-13
978-1-838472511
Paperback

Cover Design: *The communities listed in our Directory may seem very disparate and indeed they are. But they have strikingly similar elements and all have at least one thing in common. For an off-grid community it may be a canvas bender in a field... for a modern newbuild cohousing development it may be a substantial community building constructed to the highest Passivhaus standards. Whichever it is they'll all have some kind of place where people can easily get together for a cup of tea, a chat and perhaps a meal. It's what makes a community an **intentional community**.*

Distribution
Edge of Time Ltd
BCM Edge
London
WC1N 3XX
020 8133 1451

Typesetting and Layout
Jonathan How

Acknowledgements: *Thank you to all our contributors and to the many communities, housing co-ops and other organisations that have responded to our requests for information. We're very grateful to the places that have kindly hosted our editorial meetings over the last few years: Bristol Cohousing, Forgebank, Redfield, Fireside and Canon Frome.*

Contents

Preface

To dig, perhaps to dream...

Welcome, dear reader to the next exciting edition of D&D! The un-pigeon-holeable common house of the UK's intentional communities scene. This is the 12th edition – the first came out in 1989.

INTENTION: The action or fact of intending. An aim that guides action; an objective. A mental mechanism. The belief that a course of action will satisfy a desire. Exertion. Effort.

So, what has happened in the years since the previous edition? Well our culture has continued – unabated – to spew out communal living experiments all over these imaginative isles.

We've added more books to our library. *Commune on the Moors* from two founder members of Lifespan community; *Anatomy of a Commune* written by a collective of Laurieston Hall folk. Lastly, *A Life in Common*, the memoirs of our own dear Chris Coates, circling around People in Common community. We've held online book launches and are moving into YouTube.

COMMUNITY: Fellowship. A group of people living in the same locality and under the same government. The district or locality in which such a group lives. A group of people with shared values, behaviours, artefacts, benchmarks or frameworks. An exclusionary act. The benefits of belonging to a particular group are denied to non-members.

Our burgeoning social media group is heading towards 25,000 members. As for us editors: well some of us are still vagrants, others are still settled, one has left and one has joined, one of us even just became a mayor. D&D received the Kozeny Communitarian Award from the Foundation for Intentional Communities, the first time it has left the US, or gone to something other than an individual.

As is customary, the first half of this book is given over to a range of articles. In the next pages you'll go hitchhiking across the Atlantic, lift the LID on experimental planning policies in Wales, get a researcher's eye view from the latest member of the editorial collective, see exhibitions from two photographers, find out just how eco it might, or might not be to live in community *and* hear what an D&D editorial meeting actually sounds like.

INTENTIONAL COMMUNITY: /ɪnˈtenʃ(ə)nəl/ /kəˈmjuːnəti/ The belief of a group of people that by living in the same locality and under the same government their desires can be satisfied.

All good inspiration to you dear reader, to sharpen your shovel and venture forth with whatever bonkers ideas have come to you, for – as we know – 'words are not enough'.

Making Community: Is there a magic formula?

KIRSTEN STEVENS WOOD

Setting up a new community can seem a daunting and overwhelming prospect. Kirsten Stevens-Wood asks founder members of different groups how they did it and if there is anything that others might learn from their experience. What do they think helps... or hinders?

s it possible to learn from the communities that have gone before? It is certainly the case that new and forming communities are hungry for information that might assist them in their community endeavour. Between the years of 2015 and 2017 I undertook a research project that asked the question 'is there a formula to forming a sucessful community?' It often seemed that the communities I came into contact with had come into being against the odds, indeed, it is a frequently repeated statistic that only a few in every 100 groups that initially come together will get to the point of moving in together and creating a working community. In his study of 1980's communes, Benjamin Zabloki came to the conclusion that 'most' would fail, however, Ovid writing in 2013 suggested that new attempts to found communities in the eighties and nineties, had learned from the failures of the past.

It is often the case that new or emerging communities will seek out established communities to learn from, however, I now realise that the question of a single magic formula was a fairly naive one, assuming that if such a formula could be found it could then be rolled out like a recipe for others to replicate, not taking into account changing times, different goals and the complexities of the people who choose to live in community.

With that in mind, the research did produce some insights into past communities who have set out on the journey of forming a community and made the almost impossible leap to sucess (whatever success is). For this research 'success' meant

Why are Intentional Communities of interest to researchers?

Communities are often ground-breaking and experimental in their nature. Intentional communities also provide distinct environments where ideas are being tested in real time. Studies of these communities can then create a knowledge loop where researchers collect data (often by visiting or living within their communities), which they then make sense of and publish.

communities that had 'moved in' and made it past the first five years and were still up and running. My participants (18 in total) were all founder members from eight separate communities who had been involved from the start, or very early on and were still living in their respective communities (surprisingly common). For some this meant looking back almost forty years, and for others it was a more recent memory.

The interviews were often opportunistic, catching people at events and gatherings or making visits when this was possible. As such, some were recorded in quiet private rooms, but others took place in pubs, side rooms of gatherings and one on the community allotment where I was also roped into some heavy duty weed clearing. I took my short list of questions with me everywhere just in case and needed to renew my ethics approval twice as my initial plan had been to carry it all out in six months.

As with much interview based research, the results were messy. The personal stories of individuals who had thrown their lot in with a group of friends and strangers, reminiscences of close calls, strokes of luck and at times stressful encounters. Hardships and conflict were present but not overbearing in nearly all accounts, and I have to wonder if, in part, communitarians who stay have the ability to put these things behind them. For the purposes of anonymity, all names and identifying features have been changed for this article.

The core working group

In total interviews made for almost twenty hours of data which were then transcribed. A number of common themes were found. The first of these was around 'the group', or what could more accurately be described as the 'core group' or 'working group'. In all cases, regardless of the size of the final community, a smaller core or working group emerged. This was often made up of six to eight very committed individuals who brought with them either skills, knowledge or simply pure determination to make it work. The size of these core groups falls into line with other research (for example that of Wheelan, 2009) which suggests that optimum working groups are between three and eight people and that when group size increases much beyond this, levels of sociability and group productivity decreases.

From the participants I managed to interview it was also not uncommon for this core group to have been drawn from a group of friends who already had some connections and often this included pre-existing friendships and relationships:

Don't write this down but...

A surprising amount of data is collected. Some is immediately un-usable due to participants wanting to share insights, but not wanting to be quoted. It is particularly difficult to 'hide' an individual identity when researching groups who are very familiar with each other.

"Some of us knew each other already, Paula's husband worked with Tiggies brother and we had all met up quite a few times before. We joked about all living together, or buying up a row of houses and knocking them through – that's really how it all started"

"I had met Phil through my involvement with the green party and he already knew Terri because she had been active with another group that had been campaigning about the bypass, so we all sort of had these connections and some broad beliefs around environmental issues"

These core groups met more often than the wider group, undertook key functions such as property searching (if needed) and in almost every case took on the task of shaping group policies and external facing documents. They also served as the midwives of the embryonic community, supporting the wider membership, creating stability and bringing in new members when needed. Whereas wider membership often fluctuated and experienced in some cases significant turnover, the core groups tended to remain relatively stable.

Only one of the more recently formed communities bucked this trend where a single individual had actively recruited people with no prior connections via an advertisement, actively seeking out those with a similar vision. This was a notable exception and to date a sucessful community.

There is often a key individual who becomes the driver for the project.

Another commonality was that of the 'key driver' – in other words, an individual who was a member of the core group who became instrumental in taking the project forward. These people were often described in terms such as 'purposeful' and 'unwavering', these descriptions also occasionally extended to 'obstinate' or 'unrelenting'.

"Although we all worked hard, Pauline was the one who stayed with it throughout. She organised a lot of the early meetings, did a lot of the research into things like how we could buy as a collective, what our choices were. She was a bit of a powerhouse, still is"

Well written, good quality research can both provide legitimacy to new ideas (not that communities are always looking for this), which can in turn feed into legal and policy development, for example the development of the One Planet Development policy in Wales which was underpinned by living examples of low impact development, activism and research.

Interestingly, of all the founder members in this sample, it was the key driver who was more likely to leave in the early days after the community had actually moved in than any of the other founder members. Having discussed this finding with others (both academics and community members), it would be interesting to know if there is a particular personality type who is much more suited to creating community than they are to living in one. (for example, Robert McCrae and Paul Costas Five-Factor Model exploring individual traits such as openness to experience and levels of extraversion)

Helpful Outsiders

All of the founder members described the way in which external agents, who would not be joining the community, gave time, skills or knowledge to the community. In general, this came in two forms; 'experienced advisors' and 'helpful bureaucrats'. One participant described the way in which a local bank manager took them on as a sort of novelty project and lent them what (at the time) would have been way beyond the normal limits for a group like theirs. Another described the role of a solicitor who brought his experience of working with housing associations and 'undercharged' them for his time over a number of years.

One participant described the way their accountant not only prepared their accounts, but became actively involved in finding loopholes and ways of making their money go a bit further:

"Our accountant seemed to take us under his wing, he was always working out different ways that we could make this work or that happen, and I dont think he charged us for half of the work he did – he was interested you see, we were doing something a bit different and it caught his imagination"

Interestingly, a recent piece of research carried out by Melissa Fernandez and Lidewij Tummers found that with the current growth in cohousing and community led building, a new type of professional is emerging. These 'middle agents' are mediating and bridging the gap between the personalised needs of communities and the (often intransigent) world of developers, building regs and planning.

More than one of the founder members recalled the lending of money from individuals who were not part of the community either in the form of loanstock, or less formal gifts, sometimes amounting to thousands of pounds. In addition to this, one housing co-op member described the role of an external guarantor in securing their mortgage in the early days.

In many ways this illustrates the way that communities are not a closed body of people and that often their success or progression can be influenced by the generosity of others or shifts in the priorities or understanding of community led housing by successive government bodies.

Presenting as a feasible entity

Interestingly, all the community members interviewed at some point made reference to the importance of presenting a respectable 'face' when dealing with formal institutions and the surrounding community.

"Well, we couldn't go into the bank and ask for an enormous mortgage for a group called the Rainbow Hippie Convoy could we, so we went for something nice and boring, to make us look respectable"

The creation of a professional 'business like' entity enabled communities to buy property, interact with legal advisors and just as importantly create reassurance for the local community.

"we needed to get permission to make the changes we needed, and we had heard that other groups had had difficulties because of local people objecting on the basis that they were some oddball group wanting to live together. We heard after that there were rumours we were some sort of sexual cult (laughs)"

There were a few examples where community members were also members of the surrounding community, and this also appeared to reduce the surrounding communities' anxiety.

"Mike was a local councillor and both Nia and Chris had been teachers at the comprehensive, so we had some local connections that made us more respectable"

From these founder members accounts, it would appear that as well as managing internal processes such as group membership and project management, external relationship with the community and any professional services needed to be tended to. (Although not part of this research project, it is interesting to see the parallel here with more recent One Planet developments in Wales, where many low impact communities are grappling with community acceptance (and rejection in some cases) when making planning applications).

Getting the legal structure and processes right

An important theme which came up for all of the interviewees regardless of the age of the community was the importance of getting things like the legal structure of the community and the internal processes correct. One interviewee described it as setting a compass bearing on long journey – small mistakes in the early days could result in [potentially] catastrophic results a number of years down the road.

"I think that one of the reasons we have survived is that in general we got our structure right from the beginning"

"We spent a lot of time deciding on our legal ownership model as it needed the flexibility for people to be able to leave, but at the same time we needed to ensure that people leaving would not create a risk to other members. What we have now is not perfect, but it has helped us avoid the worst"

one of the reasons we have survived is that in general we got our structure right from the beginning

"Clarity over who owns what and in what way is important. People are taking a risk when they throw their lot in with a whole bunch of others and getting it clear from the beginning was essential"

However, one participant expressed how it was easy to become overwhelmed by the logistics of the buildings and other physical tasks and that 'community' could become neglected.

"We got to one point in the development where it nearly all collapsed. We had been spending so much time focusing on the building, loans and general management that we forgot why we were doing it in the first place, it was stressful and relationships suffered, it was sad to see that happen"

Many of the participants described the tightrope of maintaining a well-functioning community against trying to buy property or in some cases manage self-build projects. It is not possible from this research to put one ahead of the other – however, many of the founder members brought to the fore the fact that without a healthy, active community, a project can become meaningless or stumble due to failing membership.

Conclusions

From the accounts of the founder members who participated in this project some central messages have emerged as possible signposts to community creation

- Core groups are important, groups of between six and eight appear to be optimal.

- Not all knowledge / skills need to be found within the group

■ It is helpful to consider how a community looks to the people from the 'outside'

■ Taking time to consider how legal structures and 'sharing' will work not only in the present, but in the long term is time well spent.

Kirsten Stevens-Wood is a senior lecturer at Cardiff Metropolitan University. She is also the lead for the Intentional Communities Research Group and hosts the bi-annual Intentional Communities Symposium. In her spare time she is a bee keeper, permaculturist and woodswoman.

There appears to be no single 'magic' formula – but communities can and do learn from what has gone before, and 'communities of learning' – workshops, gatherings, information sharing - can both help inform new communities and in some cases shorten what can be a very long process. Indeed, in their three years spent visiting different communities in the 1990's Dorothy and Walter Schwarz documented a continual circle of learning within and between community through networks, writing and gatherings. Over twenty years later this networking can still be found for example the Co-Housing Network, Radical Routes and of course, Diggers and Dreamers. Drawing from organisational literature Francesca Mariotti describes learning in networks as a 'social accomplishment' where knowledge can be both constituted and also re-constituted. It may be that new intentional communities can use these collective knowledges to avoid some of the pitfalls of the past and themselves contribute to the growth of sucessful communal living.

References

1. *Arrigoitia, Melissa Fernandez & Tummers, Lidewij, 2019. Cohousing Professionals as 'Middle-Agents': Perspectives from the UK, USA and the Netherlands. Built environment (London. 1978), 45(3), pp.346–363.*

2. *Mariotti, Francesca. "Exploring Interorganizational Learning: A Review of the Literature and Future Directions." Knowledge and Process Management 19.4 (2012): 215-21. Web.*

3. *Oved, Y (2013) Globalisation of communes 1950 – 2010. London, Transaction Publishers.*

4. *Schwarz, W., and Schwarz, D (1998), Living Lightly, Charlbury: Carpenter Publishing.*

5. *Zablocki. B (1980) Alienation and Charisma: A study of contemporary American Communes. New York, Free Press.*

I Shot the Bruderhof

DANNY BURROWS

*Not many people get a chance to see inside a Christian community. In 2018
Danny Burrows was invited to take his camera along as he visited Bruderhof
communities in Australia, England, Germany, and the United States. Join him for a
behind the scenes look at another way of life.*

My first introduction to the Bruderhof was in Calais, where
they don't even have a community. At L'Auberge des
Migrants, I met their teenagers sorting donations for
"the Jungle" refugee camp. I was intrigued by their distinctive
dress and American inflection, and compelled to discover more
about a community that allowed their young people to serve in
such a demanding environment.

I would soon learn that the Bruderhof, young and old, serve
where needed: from street pastoring to most recently nursing in
Coronavirus field hospitals in New York. In short, they exercise
the selfless giving described in the Sermon on the Mount, the
cornerstone of their practice as Christians.

On my return from France I contacted the community to ask if I
could document their lives. In the spring of 2018 a dry Englishman,
who introduced himself jocularly as Brother Bernard, rang with
news: The community was going to celebrate its centennial with
a book. Would I like to be their photographer? My answer was
a swift and simple yes.

Cameras are not commonplace in the Bruderhof, and certainly
not wielded by an outsider. According to Bernard, I was the first
photographer in many years to be granted access to the community. My practice is to spend time in communities, observ-
ing and experiencing firsthand their lives. Over the next year I
documented the Bruderhof and what they describe as "another
life" in Australia, England, Germany, and the United States. It

Blessing for a new baby; Danthonia, Australia

Children learning bush craft for their twenty-four hour stay in the woods; Darvell, East Sussex

was an experience that changed my life, not only because of the incredible pictures that I was privileged to take (with the help of the author of Another Life Is Possible, Clare Stober) but also because of the positive aspects of community life that I have taken away with me. Here is a community whose members live free from the cycle of consumerism, with little reliance on the daily "smart" devices that the rest of us have come to depend on. They live in an environment where caring for each other is their principal tenet.

On my first night in Darvell, East Sussex, I was invited to a barbeque at the swimming lake, idyllic with diving boards and paddle boats. My hosts were an American chap called Greg and three generations of his family. While grilling homemade burgers we exchanged stories, sang, and played games with Greg's boys. Greg even produced a bottle of homebrew from a cooler, by which I was a little taken aback. I hadn't expected to be offered alcohol in a religious community. Greg, however, jokingly pointed out that the Bruderhof were German, which I presumed meant that beer was an intrinsic part of their culture.

I went to bed wondering if the joie de vivre I had experienced was a show, like a family might perform on the first meeting with an unfamiliar guest. Like the beer, it was not the first or last presumption about the Bruderhof that I would have to swallow.

This is not to say that life in the Bruderhof is without its struggles. Like the rest of us, they are only human. I think this is especially true in the years when young adults have to decide on a path to follow; choosing to stay in the Bruderhof means adult baptism and absolute commitment to Christ. But I have come to believe that their troubles are far fewer than those we face in the outside world.

Families live, work, and play together; their lives and the complexities of caring for the young and old are simplified by the closeness of community and the leveling effects of their community of goods. I am what some might describe as a "lefty liberal," so my opinions differ on certain more conservative values that the Bruderhof hold – but then, shared faith and egalitarian goals are certainly great values that we could all aspire to hold.

Although the communities are very different in appearance, from the rural Australian Danthonia to the stately Beech Grove in Kent, the daily routine is comparable around the globe. Families share breakfast around 7:00 a.m.; work and school begin at 8:00. At least one main meal is taken in the company of the entire community, and when the work is done families are free to do as they wish. That said, everyone, no matter their age or skill, has daily chores.

Members work in the community's fields in the early morning – each community grows some of its vegetables, fruit, and meat; Danthonia, Australia

Bruderhof school team plays the local school team in Inverell, Australia

Yet downtime is also a vital part of the Bruderhof's communal life, and a passion for the great outdoors seems to go hand-in-hand with their faith. On any given weekend in communities the world over, the crack of a bat from an impromptu softball game can be heard over the sound of band practice, choral recitals, and the chatter of kids practicing their bush craft. At the Mount Academy in upstate New York, and in the high school at Beech Grove, the trophy cabinets are literally brimming with awards won by the various teams. For a community that treasures their modesty, they sure like to win.

In Australia I stayed with the wonderful Chris and Norann and their two boys, who lived in the characterful Shanta Claire, a classic clapboard bungalow on the perimeter of the Danthonia community. They shared the house with an older couple, Jeff and Susan, who had joined the community in the sixties to live a pacifist Christian life.

Jeff is a master brewer in his spare time. On one occasion he had me sampling a pint of his latest IPA in the wee hours of the morning. Chris and Norann are both wordsmiths, and while Norann has made Shanta Claire infamous for her impromptu and joyous communal campfires, Chris and their boys are always involved in some sport.

They are all so happy at Shanta Claire, but as with every Bruderhof family, they could be called to another community and have to move at the drop of a hat. This seems an alien concept to me, but I realize that wherever they move, they are still within the broader Bruderhof family. And the concept fits with the absolute commitment they make when taking their vows in adult baptism.

The last community I visited for *Another Life Is Possible* was the small farmhouse on the outskirts of Sannerz, in Germany. This was where, in 1920, Christian theologian Eberhard Arnold and his followers created their first community, inspired by the German youth movement and modeled on the early Hutterite churches and the first church in Jerusalem. Money, property, and possessions would be shared, and service to the wider community enshrined in their way of life.

Today, in twenty-three communities around the world, the Bruderhof still live to these founding principles, bound to their neighbours by a spiritual commitment to God, humankind, and mission. I had the good fortune to visit the walled burial ground where, among other graves, the headstones of Eberhard and his wife Emmy stand, watched over by seven towering trees planted by the original community.

Christmas party in the Community Playthings' workshop – everyone enjoys a movie, barbeque, and home brew; Beech Grove, Kent

Christmas preparations in a school classroom; Darvell, East Sussex

On my last evening I walked with my host family to a spring in a nearby wood. This was where the first members were baptised. As I took a photograph of Mimi and her daughters playing on the edge of the pond, a leaf dropped into the water and created perfect ripples. I spoke about it later to Hans Brinkmann, a custodian of the German house, and he had a simple answer: "They are gifts." I knew exactly what he meant.

Those experiences in Germany were charged with love and beauty, and also a sadness that my project was coming to an end. After an incredible year documenting the Bruderhof, I could not have wished for a more fitting conclusion. But then, it was not really an end. It was really just the beginning of a turn of life's wheel.

Danny Burrows is a professional photographer and journalist whose work has appeared in GQ, Time Out, and The Guardian

Reference

1. Danny's website is at www.dannyburrowsphotography.com

A mealtime in the communal dining room; Darvell, East Sussex

Family breakfast at 6:15 a.m.; Danthonia, Australia

Bruderhof children on a bird spotting outing in upstate New York

Jenny painting at home with her cat; Fox Hill, New York

Sunday worship service; Danthonia community, Australia

A community welcomes a new baby; Bellvale, New York

Three generations of a family paint Easter eggs on a Sunday afternoon; Danthonia, Australia

Kindergarten children hearing a story; Maple Ridge, New York

Mim with her daughters at the baptism spring; Sannerz, Germany

Always coming home...

PETE LINNEL

Sometimes it's a long journey to intentional community. Inspired back in the late 1970s to look for a different way to live, Pete Linnel tells the story of his inspiration – and distance travelled – on his way to finding his dream of a low impact community.

I've been asked to furnish some backstory to this article to provide some context for my own dream of Low Impact Community...

I grew up in a small midlands market town, in a household with hundreds of books and no TV. My parents – who were children during the war against fascism and grew up with rationing and austerity – were active participants in local civil society as well as being able to grow, process and store our own fresh fruit and veg. I was introduced to direct action at a tender age by being stood in front of the grading machine – building the motorway – while the emergency archaeology team scraped and recorded another level. In my first job after school I cleaned the loos at the golf club and tried to organise my co-workers as soon as I cottoned on to what was really happening. I had discovered class awareness, and agency.

At university I did a lot of catch-up with coming of age and then spent my first summer holiday hitch-hiking around any free festivals I could find. The next year I went for Philosophy and Psychology, then transcended the syllabus with what was probably the last of Bott and Kemp's larder. The election of Thatcher was the last straw and I became what St Hunter valorised as a "Socio-economic reject" of whom there were so many it finally became fashionable to become one. I was well ahead of the curve on that...

So my post academic (drop out) world view is informed by radical thinkers and story tellers, *Alternative England and Wales* – the directory to access all areas of interesting goings on! Lloyd Khan's *Shelter* – dreaming of cabin culture and the beauty of the self build home; Illich's seminal trio – especially *Tools for Conviviality* followed by Ursula le Guin's *The Dispossessed*. I was starting to assemble a dream not only of what could be done, but of mapping the way. Meanwhile I got involved in a campaign against nuclear waste dumping in my home area; where I learned a bit about the planning system as a site of action, and how to engage local politicians and the public.

> ●●●●●●●●●●●●●●●●●
> **▐▐**
> *In the end it [Cartwheel] was killed by our own lack of preparedness as much as by the cultural shift*
> **▐▐**
> ●●●●●●●●●●●●●●●●●

My travels around Free Festivals (Festivals Archive) had shown me an ad hoc, always fluid, transgressive and radically other community- almost but not quite achieving concretisation but having a damn good time in the attempt. So when I met the Cartwheel project in the spring of 1980 I was well primed to join in. (No Link as this project has no presence on the web, but there is a note in D&D history book: *Communes Britannica*) This project was described by Benn as "A ray of hope in an age darkened by the worship of Mammon". I took an info/ recruiting stall around festivals that summer, joined the wheel roll for a few hours,

Artists impression of what Cartwheel could have looked like. From a newsletter 1980

and attended a few meetings. In the end it was killed by our own lack of preparedness as much as by the cultural shift away from allowing access to public assets like redundant airfields (eg Watchfield see free festival site).

The Cartwheel vision was what we would now identify as an intentional co-operative ecovillage community and I reckon we

This image of the main drag at Inglestone Common "New Age Gypsy Fair" in 1981 highlights the number of people living and working under canvas, rather than in vehicles.

are between us well enough ready to try again; this time with both more urgency and more hope of success. My own journey has included supporting home ed Travellers, a co-op to provide sites, running festivals, learning and teaching Permaculture, building for mates, housing co-ops and private clients,

Roots of LID policies and Welsh OPD

In the Free Festivals of the 1970s and early 80s more people lived under canvas than in motor homes. Apart from the pioneers of UK tipi living, the entry level dwelling was the traditional tinkers' bender.

Whilst at the outset this can be a very crude shelter, it is capable of refinement given time and resources; multiple rooms, split level, stone or timber flooring, windows...

Meanwhile the tipis had found a space of their own, in a remote largely isolated valley in West Wales a willing landowner sold enough land to site a handful of tipis, allowing the residents to begin to think about the future; gather a store of winter fuel, start a garden, make space for educating the children. From the start this group had no time for the authorities who came to try to chase them from the land. The policy was of relentless non-co-operation on the very reasonable grounds that they had no expectation of even a fair hearing, let alone an agreeable outcome from the planning system.

By the end of the 1980s many travelling people were living full time in benders- including those who had fully embraced the socio-economic role of itinerant rural crafts people and/or providers of services to

Two of the earliest and most refined Low Impact Development structures at Tinkers Bubble in 2004

large festivals so when the UK govt. scrapped the 1968 Act duty to provide Travellers with sites in favour of self provision a few councils looked to draw up suitable policies for non traditional Travellers.

In Somerset, the offer of a site by a philanthropist landowner led to the first attempt to gain planning consent for "experimental low impact dwellings ". Obviously it was refused, but the subsequent appeal granted consent for a limited time and subject to a set of guidelines that later became the basis of a criteria based policy adopted into the local plan.

● ● ● ● ● ● ● ● ● ● ● ● ● ● ● ● ● ●

it was still better than living at the side of the road and facing instant eviction at any time

Once the policy was adopted it became the touch stone for two projects, Tinkers' Bubble and King's Hill, both of which chose to move on and begin development prior to seeking consent. Both faced many years of legal challenge and despite the personal uncertainty this created in the lives of the participants it was still better than living at the side of the road and facing instant eviction at any time.

● ● ● ● ● ● ● ● ● ● ● ● ● ● ● ● ● ●

Benders at Kings Hill in the early years; highlighting the landscape planners nightmare of "domestic paraphernalia"

Both projects achieved consent in the end, Tinkers Bubble by the extraordinary persistence of Simon Fairlie, who of course built on the knowledge gained to become our leading theorist as well as practitioner of Low Impact Development. (Low Impact Development; Simon Failie; 2nd ed.2009) The King's Hill bender village achieved its consent largely as a result of strict adherence to a no caravans rule; thus avoiding the punitive anti-Gypsy legislation; and by having nothing of substance to lose should the council have attempted to bulldoze the site.

ll

persistence in the face of Kafkesque bureaucratic absurdity

ll

It was the practical experience of these two projects; in their explicit attempts to create a sustainable way of life for the participants which provided the greatest part of the source material informing a research project undertaken for the Welsh Government and which eventually led to the OPD policy. (Welsh LID report.) The road was never smooth, however, as Tony Wrench and "That Roundhouse" will testify (www.thatroundhouse.org.uk), but again it was persistence in the face of Kafkesque bureaucratic absurdity, as well as support of the Local Agenda 21 process, which led to eventual adoption of Pembrokeshire's Policy 52. This was the first LID policy in Wales and its adoption swiftly led to the genesis of the Lammas project- the other practical driver of the OPD policy. The Lammas planning journey is described on the website www.lammas.org.uk

Origins of One Planet Council

In November of 2013, responding to a spate of refusals of what were believed to be top quality applications for OPDs in Pembroke and Cardigan, a wide community of interest were called to meet at the Lammas Hub to discuss possible ways forward for practitioners of the policy. In his notes from the meeting Tao Wimbush sets the scene for the more than fifty who attended

"Both Local Planning Authorities and the Planning Inspectorate Wales seem to be raising the bar for OPD applications above the already high standards required by the Practice Guidance. The question presented to the meeting was – Is there something more that we can be doing to support the OPD movement in Wales?"

David Thorpe introduced us to the emerging themes discovered during research for his forthcoming book "The One Planet Life" which contributed some insight into the attitudes of the politicians at the heart of Welsh planning policy...

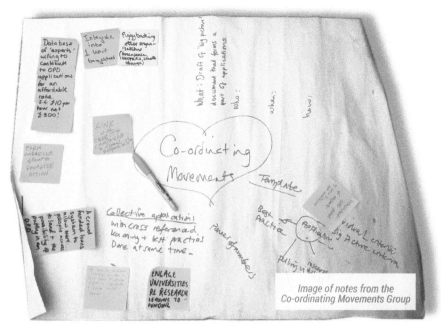

Image of notes from the
Co-ordinating Movements Group

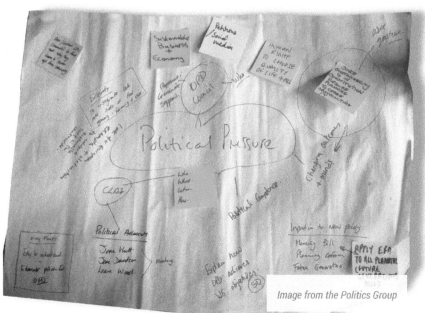

Image from the Politics Group

Notes from the Direct Action Group

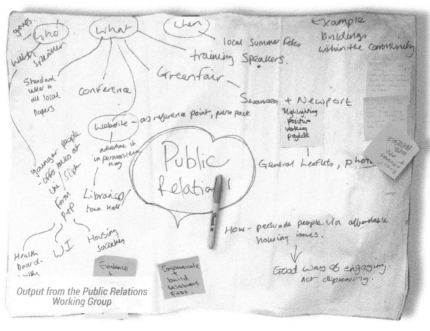

Output from the Public Relations Working Group

- Cultural Prejudice – The OPD movement is not seen as contributing to Welsh culture –and instead is seen as providing a niche opportunity for English hippies.

- Visual Impact – (both land and structures) OPD is perceived as a scruffy, cluttered and unsightly influence on the open countryside.

- Quality of Life – OPD is viewed as 'returning people to the dark ages'.

The meeting separated into a series of focussed discussion groups to explore possible future actions to overcome these perceived obstacles reporting back on topics around political pressure/ lobbying, direct action, public relations, co-ordinating movements. These images are of the mind maps generated in the discussion groups and give a flavour of the range and breadth of ideas in play.

An ad hoc committee was formed in a follow up session, which established One Planet Council as an entity leading to the website and social media presence as well as starting regular meetings at various locations around the country. Whilst most meetings have been held around the OPD heartland of West Wales there have also been meetings further afield, in Newtown and Machynlleth, among others. All meetings are open to anyone and provide valuable peer support to participants at every stage of the OPD journey. Subsequently the movement elevated an autumn meeting to the status of "Annual Gathering" creating more opportunities for extended conversations and sharing of good news, good food and of course drink.

All meetings are open to anyone and provide valuable peer support to participants at every stage of the OPD journey

OPC is now constituted as a non-incorporated voluntary body, with elected officers and a bank account to provide a governance framework in which formal actions can be taken, such as training events, ownership of IP, insurance cover and fund raising.

Among the most effective action so far by OPC has been the provision of training days for both practitioners and planning professionals dealing with OPD in their work. The training is delivered by one of the authors of the TAN6 OPD guidance and gives participants sufficient detailed exposition of the intentions and details of the guidance to inform both applicants and officers or decision makers in LPAs in how to make and evaluate an OPD application. Since inception many (but by no means all) Welsh LPAs have sent staff members to the course.

Before training, most OPD applications were routinely refused, and all early attempts had to go to appeal to get a fair hearing. After training; concurrent with LPAs gaining experience of OPD regulations more applications were passed on first presentation, including for the first time under delegated officers' powers and also the first in the Pembrokeshire Coast National Park.

Most recently the longer established OPDs have begun to host courses and training of a more practical nature- focussed on natural building and land use methods reflecting the skills and enthusiasms of the developers. Some charge a fee for expert led training whilst others offer opportunities for learning by doing- there is something for everyone. In addition a number of more experienced practitioners and theorists are now offering workshops focussed on the complex task of assembling an OPD application. At another level again are workshops looking at possible shared solutions, such as OPD on a community basis- even in terms of joint land purchase- or forming new intentional communities with an OPD focus.

Today the movement is well rooted, robust, resilient and growing rapidly as increasing numbers of projects achieve consent. There remain many LPAs, notably in the post industrial south and the affluent north east (and Snowdonia NP) with no OPDs; just waiting for that determined pioneer to have a go !

Today the movement is well rooted, robust, resilient and growing rapidly

Despite being entirely reliant on volunteers time and energy, OPC is well positioned to support novices into and through the process. Evidenced by real examples we know it is possible for someone with no prior knowledge to apply themselves to the task of securing some land, learning sufficient core skills to establish the required land based business, to design their project in terms of interconnected realms of productivity, shelter, using natural resources to generate abundance and tie all this up in a bundle as an OPD application. With every prospect of success. OPC offers support through informal discussions on social media platforms at entry level, but also

OPC is well positioned to support novices into and through the process

in response to very specific technical enquiries the growing hive mind represents an awesome reservoir of off grid/ low impact knowledge and experience, freely shared. The OPC website itself (www.oneplanetcouncil.org.uk) offers access to several levels of resources, from FAQs through position papers to shared accounts and designs for successful applications. In addition there is a curated list of experts for hire covering a range of relevant disciplines needed to compile an application- for those with more money than time for the learning curve.

In recent years some difficult challenges have emerged in meetings, at annual gatherings, and via the social media platforms. Mostly these involve issues not fully developed in the policy or its guidance notes, so in addition to continuous evolving policy discussions OPC has held ad hoc task and finish meetings to attempt solutions to questions such as

- "What happens if I get ill, injured, too old ?"

- "Why can't I live in an OPD and still be a nurse/ teacher/ blacksmith?"

Our attempts to deal with these issues are, we hope, to be fed up stream to policy makers at Welsh government level to be included in revised versions of the policy and guidance; while we hold open the possibility that larger groups at village scale could provide integrated solutions whilst keeping per capita Ecological Footprint within bounds.

At small scale local level some applicants still meet with opposi- tion or hostility from officers, members and neighbours with no understanding of the policy- or a willingness to abuse its rigour to hold back applications from unwelcome or misunderstood practitioners. We have no choice but to rely on the good faith of the planning inspectorate for equitable outcomes in such cases and so far no OPD case has gone to law for a resolution. OPC remains poised to step in when media give prominence to ill-informed statements by officials or councillors, such as this case from last year (BBC news) but we have not been quick enough to grasp wider opportunities to seize the narrative such as the case of the notori- ous Devon "Mud Hut Woman" who achieved international media notoriety in her fight for recognition of Low Impact Living.

At small scale local level some applicants still meet with opposition or hostility

OPC remains a Welsh organisation, so long as OPD as a policy is only adopted in Welsh planning. That said members are

Pete Linnel has been involved in the One Planet Council since its inception

active in the dissemination of LID and OPD policy narratives into England by providing theoretical and practical support for LID activists seeking to get policies adopted at local plan level. In reality the only proper planning policy for a state of climate emergency is one planet development with a rigorous evidence base; all new homes must be zero carbon in construction and use and surely all development should be Low Impact?

Note that all opinions expressed in this article are solely down to the author and do not represent the agreed position of One Planet Council.

Reference

1. Pete's website is at www.lifespacedesign.co.uk

A Sustainable Living Solution?

PENNY CLARK

Surely communal living is less damaging to the planet than living in an average family home? Comparing information collected from four different groups Penny Clark offers some tentative conclusions as to whether community living groups really are more sustainable.

In our current climate crisis, could community living and its associated practices be part of the answer to housing which is better for our planet as well as our sense of human connection? Community living and environmental sustainability often appear to go hand in hand, but, to what extent is this really the case? These were the questions which spurred me into doctoral research to measure the environmental impacts of four communities. Four years in, and many surveys, interviews, spreadsheets (and occasionally, weighed buckets of compost) later, results have emerged. In this article I am going to share the quantitative data I have gathered, as well as a little bit about the sustainability-related infrastructures and practices of each community.

Research Methodology

The following quantitative data were obtained through resident surveys and accessing existing records (e.g. utility bills). The data obtained was then converted into CO_2e (carbon dioxide equivalent) using multipliers from DEFRA. It should be noted that the quantitative data is therefore focused on greenhouse gases, which forms just one component of environmental sustainability (rather than others such as biodiversity, clean water and social justice, for example).

Thanks to the generosity of the communities, I was also able to obtain qualitative data using ethnographic methods. I had the opportunity to stay with the communities, spend time with residents, conduct interviews and attend activities and meetings. This helped me to contextualise the quantitative data I gathered, and understand the 'how and why?' behind the 'what?'.

Also key was having something meaningful to compare the quantitative data gathered with. Using publicly available secondary data, I configured the CO_2e emissions for the average UK single-family household. I then normalised the results from the communities to make them comparable with a household of 2.4 people (the average UK household size).

It's important to be clear that this data is subject to certain limitations. It's possible that there are errors within the data. Those who participated may not be representative of the entire community. Some of the multipliers from DEFRA are quite 'generic', and so provide a rough indication of CO_2e, rather than exact measurements. Plus, slightly different methods were used to gather data from the communities when compared with gathering data for the average UK single-family household.

Who took part?

Four communities generously opened their doors to me for this research.

Canon Frome Court (Cohousing)

Canon Frome Court is a co-operative cohousing community situated in the South West of England, home to approximately 40 adults and ten children. They live in a large Georgian manor house which is split into 20 owner-occupied units plus communal space, and they have 40 acres of land on which they collectively run a farm, which they use to produce much of their own food.

LILAC (Cohousing)

LILAC is a cohousing community based in Leeds, roughly four miles from Leeds city centre. Their site spans ¾ of a hectare of land, and they have 20 households, with a total of 50 people. The site is jointly owned through a Mutual Home Ownership Society (MHOS) model, which ensures that properties remain affordable. Their namesake, LILAC, is an acronym for 'low impact living affordable community', which summarises their community values.

Liquid Monastery (Coliving)

Liquid Monastery is a coliving community based in North London. At the time of my conducting research, there were seven people renting a four bedroom flat. The two lead tenants had retrofitted the interior of the flat, adding in more bedrooms in order to sublease the space.

The Vale (Community living)

The Vale was a six-person coliving community in South London. The residents rented a four-bedroom, four-storey semi-detached Victorian house, and originally came together over a shared interest in practicing meditation.

Results

Energy

Figure 1 shows the amount of kWh and the corresponding CO_2e for space and water heating within each community. As can be seen, all communities have a lower kWh usage and lower emissions than the average household. Of particular note is Canon Frome Court. Their retrofitted Georgian mansion is not as well insulated as a modern building, but their CO_2e emissions are the lowest. This is due to their district heating biomass boiler, which uses woodchips – a far less environmentally impactful way to heat your homes when compared with mains-supplied natural gas. LILAC's kWh are also particularly low, at just 27% of the average household's use. This purpose-built community benefits from straw bale insulation, triple glazing and draught-proof doors.

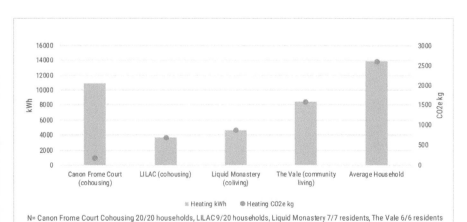

N= Canon Frome Court Cohousing 20/20 households, LILAC 9/20 households, Liquid Monastery 7/7 residents, The Vale 6/6 residents

Figure 1: Space and water heating, average per household per year

Liquid Monastery and The Vale did not have modern insulation, but benefitted from high density. The lead tenants at Liquid Monastery had cleverly retrofitted their apartment, adding an extra double bedroom to the space, therefore increasing the efficiency of their heating.

Heat-saving practices were also key: putting heating on timers, having a maximum setting on the thermostat, and putting on an extra jumper were all par for the course.

Figure 2 shows kWh of electricity and the attached CO_2e emissions for each community. Once again, all communities have lower electricity use and lower CO_2e emissions than the average household. Canon Frome Court and LILAC benefit from solar PV, and also sell some of their electricity back to the grid. Liquid Monastery and The Vale once again lower their usage through higher density of household members. Liquid Monastery in particular did not possess any large, power-hungry TVs or sound systems, which may also account for their particularly low electricity usage.

A tension that arose within communities was that residents wanted to make people feel welcome – in part through creating light, warm spaces – whilst also wanting to conserve energy. Residents used a number of strategies to try and fulfil both criteria, such as motion sensor lights, heating only the rooms that people were in, and offering slippers and cardigans to guests, rather than turning up the thermostat! At Canon Frome Court, for example, individuals were empowered to heat spaces only

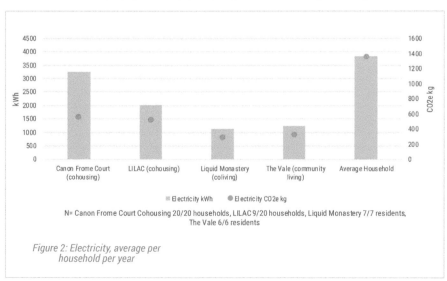

Figure 2: Electricity, average per household per year

when needed through the use of clear written instructions within communal areas.

Food

Figure 3 shows how much food in weight the average household purchased, grew or produced per year, and the associated CO_2e emissions. The graph shows that all communities aside from Canon Frome Court purchased, grew or produced a similar amount of food to the average household. Canon Frome Court's difference may be explained by the high amount of food grown and produced on site, which, according to the data gathered at the time (during November) was just under 50%. This would be likely to reduce both food waste and food packaging.

The most notable difference between the communities and the average household is the amount of CO_2e emissions attached to this food. This is due to the amount of meat consumed by residents.

All residents had lower than average levels of meat consumption, which significantly lowers CO_2e impacts. Vegans, for example, can expect to have 40% of CO_2e impact of those who eat on average over 100 grams of meat per day.

In both LILAC and The Vale, shared meals were always vegan in order to be inclusive. Those who did eat meat reported cutting down since moving to their community due to the influence of

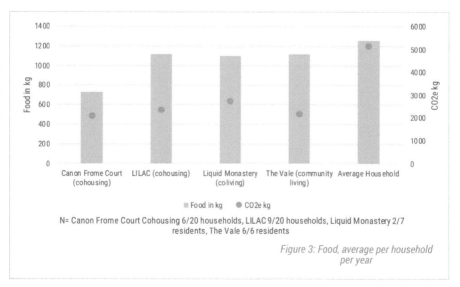

N= Canon Frome Court Cohousing 6/20 households, LILAC 9/20 households, Liquid Monastery 2/7 residents, The Vale 6/6 residents

Figure 3: Food, average per household per year

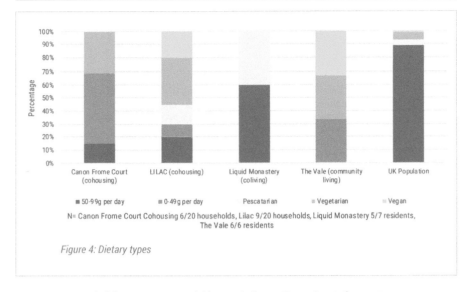

N= Canon Frome Court Cohousing 6/20 households, Lilac 9/20 households, Liquid Monastery 5/7 residents, The Vale 6/6 residents

Figure 4: Dietary types

their housemates or neighbours. At Canon Frome Court, the meat that was consumed tended to be from the on-site farm, and so in most regards had a lower environmental impact than meat purchased from a supermarket.

One thing that the quantitative data does not capture is the care that was frequently taken by the communities in trying to source local, ethically-produced food. This will most likely have further lowered the CO_2e impacts of participants' diets.

As most communards will know, food and communal meals are hugely important to most communities. They are spaces where residents can catch up with one another and share their lives, as well as ideas and experiences. Food also becomes an important expression of shared values, such as localism, autonomy and ethical, socially just consumption.

Travel

Figure 5 shows that of the four communities, Canon Frome Court is the only one which has higher than average emissions when compared with the average household, for both commuting and non-commuting purposes. The other three communities have significantly lower than average emissions. These differences are due to location. Canon Frome Court is situated rurally, with no immediate public transport links and roads that are unsafe to cycle on. LILAC is based in outer Leeds, and has a cycle path

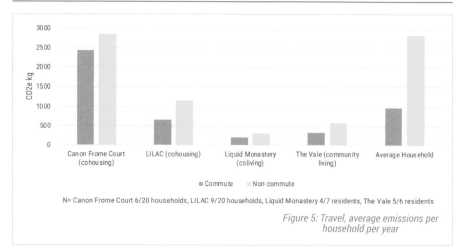

N= Canon Frome Court 6/20 households, LILAC 9/20 households, Liquid Monastery 4/7 residents, The Vale 5/6 residents

Figure 5: Travel, average emissions per household per year

to the city centre, plus readily available buses. Liquid Monastery and The Vale are both in London Zone 2, where there is highly convenient public transport, ample cycle lanes and furthermore, where there are greater practical, economic, and norms-based barriers to private car ownership.

Within these enabling and constraining infrastructures, each community has taken actions which lower the emissions from their transport. All communities with cars engaged in car-sharing, with the two cohousing communities both having carpools (in fact, after I gathered this data, Canon Frome Court set up a carpool with four electric cars, so it is likely their travel emissions are now a fair bit lower). Both LILAC and Liquid Monastery have strong

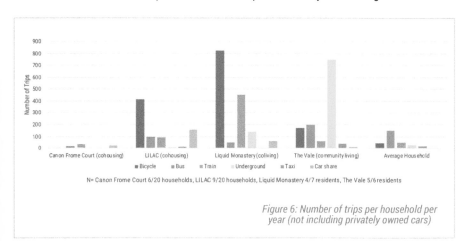

N= Canon Frome Court 6/20 households, LILAC 9/20 households, Liquid Monastery 4/7 residents, The Vale 5/6 residents

Figure 6: Number of trips per household per year (not including privately owned cars)

cycling cultures, with good cycle storage, available equipment and know-how for the maintenance of bicycles, and the option to borrow bicycles from one another. Many residents reported that the example set by others in the community encouraged them to cycle more.

Figure 6 shows the number of trips made by transport mode other than cars. Here the high number of cycling trips made by LILAC and Liquid Monastery members can clearly be seen. The two London-based communities, Liquid Monastery and The Vale, rely heavily on transport by train or by underground. Compared with all other communities, LILAC has a higher number of journeys made by car share.

Figure 7 shows the average number of aeroplane flights and the associated average CO_2e emissions each household within each community took. Within most communities there was, to a certain extent, a culture of not flying for environmental reasons. The exception to this rule was Liquid Monastery. In part this was due to Liquid Monastery residents being from countries other than the UK, meaning that they flew more often to visit family or for work-related purposes. Furthermore, Liquid Monastery residents appreciated holidays as a welcome break from their intense work schedules. Though some residents did report feelings of guilt over the frequent flights that they took .

Within the other communities there was a variety of attitudes and practices to flying. To some residents, taking a flight to go on holiday was normal, some would not fly at all, and oth-

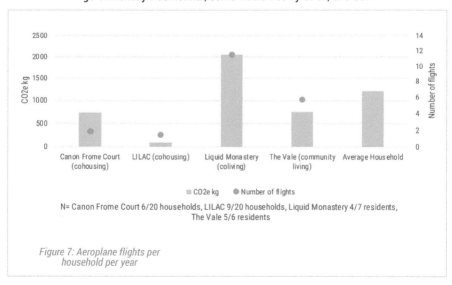

N= Canon Frome Court 6/20 households, LILAC 9/20 households, Liquid Monastery 4/7 residents, The Vale 5/6 residents

Figure 7: Aeroplane flights per household per year

ers would make attempts to minimize their flights e.g. take the train one way and fly back. Residents of LILAC reported a culture of minimizing flights, which meant that people who did fly sometimes associated this with feelings of guilt, and that holidays to exotic locations did not have the usual meanings of prestige that they would within a 'mainstream' setting. Similarly, residents of The Vale reported anti-flight attitudes spreading amongst their household during the years that they lived together. As can be seen from Figure 7, flights have a high carbon cost. Liquid Monastery's flights made up a whopping 30% of their total CO_2e emissions (a figure which is partly due to how low their CO_2e emissions were in other areas). Yet, this shows that minimizing or forgoing flights is a good way to cut your greenhouse gas emissions.

Purchases

Emissions which occur along the supply chains of the items that we buy make up a significant amount our overall CO_2e. Communities, with their emphasis on sharing, have the potential to significantly lower this carbon cost, as Figure 8 indicates. The research found that all communities estimated their purchases to be significantly lower than the average single-family household.

There were a number of ways in which being part of a community minimized purchases. In all communities there was a culture of sharing items, either through informal borrowing, or through having communal possessions, such as tools, kitchenware or

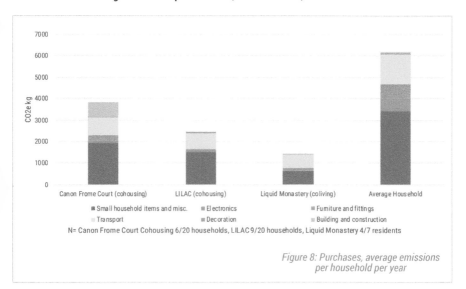

Figure 8: Purchases, average emissions per household per year

larger items like lawnmowers, washing machines and bicycles. In some cases, such as Liquid Monastery, a smaller amount of private space meant that it simply wasn't possible to have a lot of possessions.

There also tended to be a culture of 'make-do-and-mend', which was furthermore enabled by residents pooling their knowledge and skills on repairs and maintenance of items. Anti-consumerist values also shifted expectations and norms around the link between ownership of expensive items and success. As such, buying secondhand or buying less was generally the norm. An example one LILAC resident gave is that within the community, she could wear the same party dress to any number of occasions without feeling self-conscious about it.

Waste

Figure 9 shows that all communities produce significantly less non-recyclable waste than the average household, but the same or more amounts of dry recycling and compost. In particular, Canon Frome Court produces a large amount of compost per household, due to its farm.

Within all communities certain waste-saving practices existed. LILAC and Canon Frome Court's food growing played an important role in lowering non-recyclable and dry recyclable waste. In both The Vale and LILAC, joint bulk food purchases also minimized waste from food packaging, whilst a food market near to Liquid

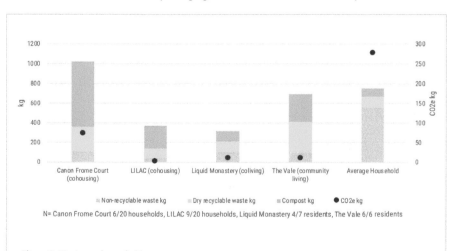

Figure 9: Waste per household per year

Monastery meant that residents could easily purchase fruits and vegetables that were not wrapped in plastic. Furthermore, Liquid Monastery residents reported that their limited kitchen storage space encouraged thoughtful food purchases, leading to less food waste. Practices such as repurposing old items, from making furniture from old pine boards to turning old newspapers into paper bags, also played a part in lowering overall waste.

In part, the low CO_2e emissions arising from waste were due to careful waste management from all communities. However, it is important to note that waste infrastructure had a significant role to play. Both London and Leeds incinerate the majority of their non-recyclable waste, which has a much lower CO_2e impact than putting waste in landfill.

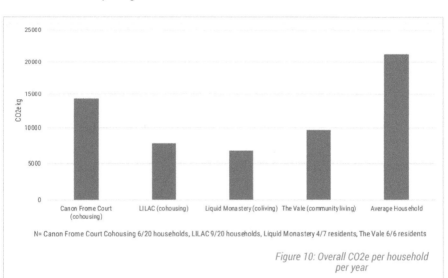

N= Canon Frome Court Cohousing 6/20 households, LILAC 9/20 households, Liquid Monastery 4/7 residents, The Vale 6/6 residents

Figure 10: Overall CO2e per household per year

In Summary

Figure 10 shows the overall CO_2e kg for the four case study communities broken down by each emissions stream, with the average UK single-family household as a comparison point. All case studies have significantly lower yearly emissions than the average single-family home, with Canon Frome Court's emissions at 67% of the average home, Liquid Monastery at 32%, LILAC at 37% and The Vale at 45%.

Four case studies are not enough to make generalisations about all communities. However, by linking together infrastructures and practices with resulting CO_2e emissions, we can have some understanding of their greenhouse gas-lowering benefits, which may enable us to make reasonable assumptions about other, similar communities.

In conclusion: beyond the numbers

> *communities may act to create a shared culture which allows residents to redefine what a prosperous life is*

During this research, I have learned that community and environmental sustainability are deeply intertwined. Sharing is at the heart of the matter – whether that's sharing in spaces, environmental ideals, or engaging in the shared governance which enables coordination of resources and sustainability-related projects to take place. Importantly, communities may act to create a shared culture which allows residents to redefine what a prosperous life is. Homes which enable fulfilling social connections and shared, meaningful endeavour with others encourages a contentedness; which in turn mitigates against the desire to rampantly consume, or to temporarily escape to faraway places. This more affordable lifestyle means less pressure to make ends meet, and so more space for work to be values-driven rather than money-driven. And indeed, it takes work, time and sometimes money to set up carpools, jointly purchase an eco-friendly boiler, plan a system to bulk buy food together, and all the other myriad projects that living with a group of likeminded people can enable. Could community living and its associated practices be part of the answer to the climate crisis? As I see it, the meaningful work, connection with others and the low impact on our planet that I have seen in these communities is a hopeful blueprint for a culture that we need to transition to, to secure a sustainable and just prosperity for our planet.

Penny Clark is a doctoral researcher, exploring environmentally sustainable practice within UK cohousing and coliving communities. She is also a co-founder of Conscious Coliving, a consultancy and research body which aims to promote and embed social value within the coliving sector.

Settlements

DAVID SPERO

A chance meeting at the Glastonbury Festival led to an extended trip through the world of UK based low-impact off-grid intentional communities. The resulting extensive photographic record of these groups charts the evolution and growth of these distinct forms of community.

O n a warm summers evening, I lay hidden with two friends behind a hedge just one field away from the perimeter fence surrounding the 25th Glastonbury festival. Scrambling through a gap in the hedge, we make a carefully timed dash, evading stewards patrolling in Land Rovers fitted with searchlights, to the base of a three-meter high steel security fence. We throw our bags towards the starlit sky and watch as they arc over the fence and thud to the ground. My accomplices interlink fingers forming steps to propel me to the top. From there I helped to pull them up and then two long bruising minutes later we were all safely on the other side!

It was June 1995 and I was two years on from completing a photography course in London and slowly finding my way into making a freelance living from the craft of taking and fixing images onto film. This work was a means to an end, supporting and giving me time to follow and explore my own photographic path in parallel. This path was about to be altered by what was either chance or serendipity.

A friend had been telling me about Permaculture and its philosophy of working with, rather than against nature. On their recommendation I went for a walk in the festivals Permaculture Garden. There I met a group of people who had built a demonstration low-impact 'bender' dwelling made of bent and tied hazel-wood poles covered with insulation and canvas. I stopped to talk and they told me about their plans to collectively purchase some land to set up a small, land-based community to explore low-impact living along with permaculture.

At that time, I was working on a number of inter-connected photographic series documenting landscapes and structures that reflected exploitative and controlling relationships to the natural environment and its resources. These series revealed and recorded cultures that isolate us from, and subtly dictate our relationship with, the environment and each other. The simple bender structure in the permaculture garden, with its greater openness to the environment, and the closer, more constructive and sustainable engagement with the natural environment desired by its residents represented an alternative way of existing. Living in balance with, and having a more open connection to, the surrounding ecosystem, in a less controlling and exploitative relationship.

'The Longhouse' communal space and workshop (view from old kitchen path), Steward Community Woodland, Devon, June 2004

Canvas-covered structure, part hazel pole bender and part roundwood timber frame, with reused materials. Initial construction 2000

That meeting and the image of the bender stayed with me as I worked on various projects over the following years. Then in 2002 a couple of life's threads came together to take the meeting in the permaculture garden forward. I had begun to swim in freshwater lakes and rivers throughout the year, and found myself experiencing an extremely immediate, physical form of connection with the surrounding organic environment, literally immersing myself within it. These regular immersions led me to reflect on how the structures we build isolate us from the organic environment that surrounds us, cutting us off from the effects of a more sensual exposure to the surrounding natural environment.

At the same time I was working on a series of photographs of churches in London, housed in buildings never originally constructed to be churches, and converted to new, non-secular uses. Unlike traditional churches, the architecture, beyond the need for four walls and a roof, had become redundant and accidental.

Tony and Faith's, Brithdir Mawr,
Pembrokeshire, July 2005
Roundwood timber-frame roundhouse with cobwood
walls and turf-covered reciprocal frame roof.
Constructed 1997-98

I began to draw and trace connections between these 'secular' church buildings and self-built, low impact structures. Both were recycled, makeshift and pragmatic, and unconcerned with consumer values, status and mainstream aesthetics. I found myself thinking more and more about the embryonic community I had met in the permaculture garden, and wondering what they had gone on to build. Early in 2004, through searching for that community, I got in touch with a small number of low impact settlements. That June I found myself walking up a winding woodland track and across a bubbling stream to Steward Community Woodland for a visitor's work weekend. There, along with helping to construct deer fences, I took the first photograph of the *Settlements* project (see page 50). Later that year I visited Tinkers Bubble, Brithdir Mawr, a number of 'locations undisclosed' and the following year Landmatters.

Mike's, Tir Ysbrydol, Brithdir Mawr,
Pembrokeshire May 2014
Cob-rendered straw bale hut with turf-covered
reciprocal frame roof. Constructed by James 2012

Originally, I set out to document the structures set within the landscape using a typological photographic approach similar to the one I was using to photograph the churches. But this changed and expanded in response to what had been built and as relationships grew and deepened. I soon began to photograph infrastructure, food growing areas and interiors, and then community portraits.

Visits became more frequent and I would both photograph and volunteer. I've weeded, planted, harvested and shared communal meals made with food grown and freshly picked from the gardens. I've milked cows and chased them across fields to round them up when they'd worked out how to jump the solar-powered electric fence. I've ridden to the village pub by horse and cart down country lanes bathed in moonlight. I've woken at 4 a.m. to

Rooh's, Landmatters, Devon, May 2008
Canvas-covered hazel pole bender. Constructed 2005

scythe hay on glorious summer days, fueled by homemade bread with cheese. All washed down with homemade cider under shady trees in the late afternoon. I've slipped around in the mud on a rain-soaked February coppicing weekend, hand-sawing trees with bow-saws till exhausted, and then rejuvenated by a communal roast dinner to celebrate the work done. I've celebrated birthdays, weddings and community anniversaries, watched children grow and flourish, and made many good friends.

What I thought would be one year and 20 photographs, had become on publication in 2017, thirteen wonderful years and 150 photographs charting the communities' evolution and growth. Work on the book started in 2009 when *Settlements* was nominated for a photography book publishing award. This

John, Sonia, Daisy, Marley and Asha's,
Steward Community Woodland, Devon, June 2008

required me to put together a book dummy sequence. From the 70-80 photographs I had at the time, I worked out a structure that could combine the projects different visual elements along with accompanying texts. In 2012 I began writing what became around 18,000 words that explore connected historical and contemporary issues ranging from the Enclosures to industrialisation, post war planning, land control, low impact architecture, ecocide and the anthropocene age. I also invited a member from each community to write an introduction giving an account of their aims, governance, history and economy.

By the end of 2015 with the writing almost complete and a full set of analogue C-type hand prints that i'd meticulously printed, I was ready to start the publishing production process; scanning,

Mary and Joe's, Tinkers Bubble, Somerset, June 2004
Roundwood and sawn timber-frame house with
thatched roof and waney board cladding. Constructed
by Simon and Mary 2001

proofing, proofreading, book design and the final layout. At that time I had been in discussion with a publisher, but the compromise and cost was too high and I decided to explore the DIY route and self-publish with a Kickstarter campaign. Then in January 2016 luck came my way. I received an email from the Victoria & Albert Museum with the welcome news that a submission to their Photographs Acquisition Group, I had been invited to make 6 months earlier had been selected for purchase. This along with a few loans meant I could go ahead and publish.

Settlements rolled off the press in Dorchester in February 2017 over two long days in which the printers worked tirelessly to perfectly ink each of the 32 metal plates, as the paper sped through. Over the next couple of week's the sheets were cut, gathered, section stitched and bound into a beautiful hard cover book. I was now a book seller!

Community portrait,
Steward Community Woodland, Devon, May 2015
Without Chris, Owen and Aaron. 15th anniversary

The final writing ahead of the books 'copy' deadline 31st August 2016 was a 'Planning update'. This was to cover any news from the community introduction sign-off dates, which ranged from July 2014 to February 2015, till the 'copy' deadline. Most of the updates were good news. Landmatters secured permanent planning permission without any objections. Temporary permissions were granted at Tinkers Bubble for a further 10 years and at Brithdir Mawr for a further three years. But the final update from Steward Community Woodland was devastating.

In 2015, after 15 years of living precariously on hard-won temporary permission, the community applied to Dartmoor National Park Authority for permanent permission under their new low-impact development policy DMD 30 introduced to help low-impact initiatives get planning permission. The park refused permission so the community appealed to the planning inspectorate. On the

Fire pit, looking towards the sight of 'The Longhouse', Steward Community Woodland, Devon, November 2018
Court Injunction compliance period

David Spero *is a British photographer known for his quietly contemplative enquiries into overlooked communities and the appropriation of space. For Settlements, Spero spent ten years documenting communities that aim to live with minimal impact on the environment.*

10th August 2016, after a 5 day public inquiry held over April and May, the planning inspector dismissed the appeal.

A community dedicated to protecting the environment through demonstrating ecologically low-impact ways of living was to be removed in order to protect the view from a short section of the A382, between the sewage works and a rifle range, on the edge of Mortonhampstead. A view from which it was practically invisible.

Settlements has been ongoing since publication with the most recent photographs taken at Steward Community Woodland during the compliance periods of four Enforcement Notices in 2017 and a court injunction served in October 2018 (see page 57). By the injunction compliance date of 7th April 2019 all eight households that formed the community had dismantled their homes and found accommodation elsewhere.

Reference

1. *David's website is at www.davidspero.co.uk*

Haymaking, Tinkers Bubble, Somerset, July 2005

Cath's Epic Journey

CATH MULLER

Cath wanted to see if there were radical projects outside of the UK that we might learn from. She also wanted to visit them without contributing to the destruction of the planet. Join her as she set out on a Year of Searching for Anarchist Utopias.

Oct 25 2017:

After a year of preparation, including sailing training (with The Sailboat Project) and learning Spanish, I left Cornerstone Housing Co-op and Footprint Workers Co-op in Leeds and set off on a mission.

My mission: to seek out alternative co-operative economies, social currencies and crypto-currencies, particularly radical worker co-operatives embedding worker co-operation in strategies for social change – in Barcelona and North America, without flying.

With 20+ years of communal living in a Radical Routes co-op under my belt, and not much cash to splash, I also made good use of intentional community networks and comrades to find places to stay.

A hiccup in the schedule

The plan:

- match-make a lift across the Atlantic via an online crewing forum

- stay in Barcelona until late November (end of the hurricane season)

■ meet the boat late Nov and nip over the pond arriving Stateside around New Year

■ find a lift back in early July (just before the next hurricane season)

But all of this depended on getting a visa...

... you see, you can't just get any old quickie UK privilege tourist visa if you want to arrive in the US by yacht and maybe work for cash. So I went for a 'J visa', used for exchange programmes. I finally found a helpful worker co-op academic at the Uni of Massachusetts to sponsor me and started the process in early September. It turns out that getting one of these visas is a) a bit complicated, b) expensive and c) prone to getting stuck at any/ all stages. I set off for Barcelona at the end of October, thinking maybe it would take another couple of weeks.

Problem: I couldn't arrange a lift until I had the visa and I ended up in limbo in Barcelona for two months. The paperwork came through in time for me to book a Madrid visa interview on 6th Jan. By 10th January I got to the coast to start hitching! Could I still make up some time and stick to my plan?

Limbo in Spain

I landed in Barcelona at Can Masdeu, a well-known and established squat, land project, intentional community and social centre in the hills.

The first week I was joined by Radical Routes buddies to meet the Catalan Integral Co-op (CIC) and learn about their local currency & supply chains and the FairCoin co-op crypto-currency. We visited the Can Batllo ex-factory site and now co-op development hub and the site of La Borda, a massive new-build housing co-op.

It was right in the middle of the Catalonia independence protests. I spent a lot of time at Aurea Social, the CIC HQ – offices, exercise studios, consulting rooms and radical co-operators & tech activists from all over the world. Some days we visited squats & social centres (there are scores of them!), other days interviews with architects' workers co-ops, a phone & broadband co-op, radical bookshop collectives. Tours of community gardens, marches and blockades for independence at the Sagrada Familia, hanging out in co-op bars and clubs, making beer, giving workshops on the UK housing co-op model at the fortnightly Can Masdeu 'PIC' political festival, helping on the workdays.

I went to Can Tonal, a 3-year old income-sharing community of 12 people, set up as part of a looser income-sharing network (Vallbona Mutual Aid) around the village of Sant Antoni, building local resilience and developing culture and traditions around seasonal events.

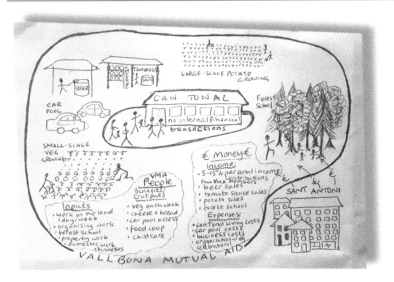

And a great workday at Colonia Vidal, a purpose-built 19th C abandoned factory village being handed over to ex-Can Masdeu folks to create a huge new community, Vidalia.

In Madrid for my visa interview, I stayed with a dispersed permaculture community in Perales de Tajuña who distribute their produce in Madrid via a radical local currency, La Canica. We also went to do some gardening at Garaldea, a community squatting in a former juvenile mental health institution and focusing on radical education and support.

I headed to the coast via Marinaleda, a communist village in Andalucia managed partly by an autocratic mayor, partly by community assembly. On land they seized from the local aristo after the fall of Franco, they have a giant co-op where everyone works producing canned artichokes and tomatoes and co-op members have a right to super-cheap housing. [pics of artichokes and breaking free fists on mayor's desk]

I hung out at marinas at Malaga, Gibralta and Cadiz, conspicuously reading 'Competent Crew Skills' [PIC] - but it was too late in the season and Americas-bound sailors had all left 6 weeks earlier. So I gave up on the mainland and got a 2-day ferry to the Canary Islands.

How to hitch across the ocean

Las Palmas is the last port of call for all trans-Atlantic crossings, the place for last-minute maintenance, replacement parts and stocking up on 6 weeks' worth of food & water. So it's also a honeypot for dozens of hitchers buzzing around looking for lifts. Folks were squatting, camping on the beach and busking to survive – some had been waiting there 2 months, including a guy who'd come on a scooter from East Asia.

While boat-seeking, I met the awesome Federacion Anarquista de Gran Canaria, who helped 70 families to squat a block of flats, La Esperanza, part of the PAH, the massive Spanish squatting and anti-eviction movement since the 2008 crash. I also went to a conference on community power and anti-touristification.

Within 5 days I found Atlantic-novice Guy (French) and his 10.2m yacht, Igavik. #3 crew was Spanish Dani, who'd never been on a boat, and luckily we found German Robin, who was logging nautical miles for his Oceanmaster certificate. Having spent all our money on boat-fixing, food, water, life-jackets and sunglasses, we set off into the rain, wind and sea-sickness on 31st January and arrived in the Caribbean 25 days later – still over 1500 miles south of the US.

As we arrived, I was desperate to get online and find my next lift north. Then I spotted this logo on a boat 2 moorings along and went to meet Rainer. Rainer was US-bound! Whoop! 3 days in, Rainer & I joined Franko's boat and island-hopped for weeks until, in Puerto Rico, I finally jumped ship for Tom's boat. So it took 45 more days before I landed in North Carolina, 15th April. I was 4 months behind schedule and no one in the US even knew I was coming – first task, find somewhere to stay..

North America in Community

Almost my first stop (even before getting to UMass Amherst to officially be in the country) was at Twin Oaks community in Virginia. TO is the original egalitarian community inspired by the utopia described in 'Walden Two' by BF Skinner. Set up in 1967, other egalitarian communities have learnt many of its lessons. Of the 7 or so communities within 10 miles, I also visited Acorn, Cambia and Living Energy Farm. All are fully income-sharing, varying from 6 adults through 30-ish to about 90 at TO when I was there. TO is structured as a worker-owned co-operative – the members work and, in return, all their (and their kids') needs are met, including 2 cooked meals/day. Healthy adults work 42 hrs/wk – which includes all business, domestic, land and community work (meetings, labour exchanges, political acitivity, social organising). Acorn's main income-generating business is seed production and TO's main businesses are hammock- and tofu-production and the distribution of Acorn's seeds. There's so much more to say, but no room – I loved it there.

TO was a founding member of the Federation of Egalitarian Communities (FEC) and is a very active member of the Federation of Intentional Communities. In 2017, ex-Acorners and TO'ers started 'Point A', a project to set up urban FEC communities, because the majority of folks in N America live in cities. I stayed at Compersia in Washington DC. It was small (7-8 adults?) and trying hard, but being income-sharing in a big city, with all its distractions and commerce, is incredibly difficult. I believe Compersia is now down to 3 adults and the other two Point A communities (in NYC and Portland OR) have both folded.

One FEC associate bucks the trend though – in late May I stayed at Ganas on Staten Island, NYC, for about a week. Founded in the mid-80s, it's a hybrid with an income-sharing core group of about 12 people, 3 2nd-hand shops and 60ish rent-paying members in a community focused on interpersonal communication. I nearly jacked in the whole trip to stay there as my mental health was so frazzled at that point.

Other highlights: Love & Solidarity community in DC, The Hive co-op in Ann Arbor, Michigan (I introduced them to The Hive in Bradford in a Zoom) and Riot Bayit, a nascent urban kibbutz community in Somerville, Boston, where I joined their open Friday-night meal & discussion to talk about my travels and discuss the politics of communalism & social change.

Co-operative Training Grounds

As my sofa-surfing connections got more spontaneous and tangential I ended up visiting my first student housing co-op (SHC) in Austin, Texas. My friend-of-a-friend-of-a-friend host had graduated to La Reunion Co-op, but he was still proud of 21st Street Co-op and took me for a tour of it.

SHCs are a training ground for co-operation, self-responsibility and business management. This is why the UK co-op movement is so excited about the birth of SHCs over here, particularly Student Co-op Homes, a secondary co-op to support the new primary co-ops. However the UK co-ops are mostly still small – 7 people in Sheffield, 12 in Birmingham, etc. 21st Street, at 100 members seems about average for SHCs over the pond.

Architecturally compared to a tree-house, 21st Street describes itself as the 'proudest, weirdest and perhaps the most storied co-op... also the only clothing-optional co-op' of the Austin SHCs. In fact it's notorious across the continent, for outrageous behaviour and an almost cultish sense of identity. I loved it – I loved the sense that any limits were imposed by the co-op rather than social norms and the fierce focus on self-responsibility and community accountability. The co-op is particularly strict about missing shifts or other commitments, which feels really rare.

My time in Berkeley California coincided both with a friend's arrival (from Edinburgh SHC) to live in Lothlorien SHC and also with the Berkeley student co-op managers conference - not just an opportunity to tour some of Berkeley Student Co-operative's 20 co-ops (founded in the '30s, housing 1260 students – biggest in N.America), but also to meet staff from across the US and Canada. Result!

And as a result I stayed at, spoke at or dined at The Bower (E. Lansing, Michigan), Nottingham (now Phoenix) Co-op (Madison, Wisconsin), the Inter-Community Co-op Council (Ann Arbor, Michigan), the Circle Pines Co-op Centre (an absolute delight in Michigan) at a training event for new student housing co-op board members, WCRI co-op in Waterloo-Kitchener Ontario (2nd biggest) and Neill-Wycik Co-op College in Toronto (3rd biggest). All across the movement, people were struggling to keep, or in some cases recreate, a co-operative culture, a sense of agency and responsibility – it was fascinating to talk through how you might engender that in a co-op that had become a soulless tower block of 750 individual rooms with limited common areas, a catered cafe and security staff ID-ing everyone who comes in the front door.

Comfort and Security

Standard interaction: 'Hey, you should meet my really cool friend, who lives in this great co-housing project' - 'yes! I'd love to! Do they have a common room where I could do a talk?'

Initially I hadn't been much interested in co-housing, because it often seems more about comfort and security for those who can afford it. But, as with all projects outside the norm, they need to overcome political, inter-personal and financial obstacles and the pioneers of each project have a vision of a better world and some pretty useful experience to share.

Many also partially fill the social/political/educational gaps left by the demise of religious & cultural institutions, with space in their common houses and meeting rooms for socials, meetings, playgroups, food co-ops, etc. In my case, they provided free public space, a ready-made audience of like-minded people and, at Burlington Co-Housing, Vermont, a bed too.

Projects are always intertwined, everything is part of an eco-system of relationships:

I go to meet Sassafras Tech Collective in Ann Arbor and Tom says 'come have dinner with us at Touchstone', while Fuzzy from The Hive suggests I talk at Sunward's weekly random speakers morning & lunch.

I make contact with Jerry & Ted from Sociocracy for All in Amherst MA, and arrange to meet at the Pioneer Valley Co-housing common house – a fabulous, octagonal, wooden building with large central hall going up two floors. We finish as the sound check for the gig starts.

Winslow Co-Housing: yep, all co-housing projects have lovely trees and flowers

An old friend on Bainbridge Island, Seattle introduces me to his cool new friend who lives at Winslow Co-Housing. And the

cool new friend says, 'you must know my childhood friend, who used to live in Equinox Housing Co-op in Manchester – now she's married to a First Nations chief and they're all coming for lunch tomorrow'. Incredible synchronicity and wonderful opportunities to meet new people and learn.

Housing: just one part of a grand plan...

I discovered a delightful series of films made by Craig at Fair-Op in Lewiston Maine: 'My So-called Housing Co-op', about the evolving community in a young housing co-op with 3 flats. When I got there to stay with them, the Fair-Op had been used to create RAISE-Op: now 15 flats and truly multi-ethnic and afford-able. It is a feat of community organising and political ambition – and part of an incred-ible co-operative economy- and community-building effort there. This great article from 2019 covers all the good stuff: https://s.coop/lewistonauburnmigrantsandcoops

This is exactly the kind of thing I was looking for: where co-operative homes are just one element of a grander plan for sustainable, integrated, socially just communities.

I visited Co-operation Jackson in Mississippi to find out more about their black-led, city-scale organising of housing, workers co-ops, general assemblies and municipal political activity and their aim of creating a human rights city.

I found myself immersed in a heart-breaking and rage-inducing history of struggle and racist oppression. As they make more gains (a supermarket here, a factory unit there, some more empty plots, a growing farming business) and grow their resources and power, they are aware of the open and covert ways that they will be targetted to block their progress. I am inspired by them and at the same time scared for them.

Glaring inequality and injustice was all around and at the forefront of conversations during my time in North America... and I could write another 8 pages about that! Suffice to say that it helped me see the UK's own issues around race with fresh eyes.

Going home and going forward

Leeds Cath @leedscath   3d
Crazy idea(worrying I won't find a way to sail home)wot about sailing a boatfull of rad US books/mags, US-Eur Oct/Nov18? needs buyers! a boat/skipper! @SailBoatProject @AKEdinburgh @Activedistro @gringoben @voyage_vert @LucyGilliam @Oceanpreneur @NewDawnTraders @iwsa_secretary

Cath Muller Since 1995, Leeds Cath has lived communally in Cornerstone Housing Co-op and been an active member of the Radical Routes federation of co-ops working for social change. She is a founding member of Footprint Workers Co-op and a member of the Worker Co-op Council of Co-operatives UK.

So what then did I do about being 4 months late into a 6-month tour? Well, I wasn't going to cut my trip short! I did valiantly try to find a way to get home without flying (see tweet), but they were only up for taking the books, not me. So I decided to get as close to home as possible and booked a flight from Halifax, Nova Scotia. £178 for six hours, as opposed to about £2500 and 3 months. Hmm.

And what will I do with all my learnings, reflections, connections? Having given myself a year's worth of confirmation bias, I am even more convinced that collective solutions can help us survive the ecological, economic and social disasters that beset us. Communal and co-operative living practically minimises our contribution to capitalism and exploitation. But not by itself – community-level supply chains, energy production ad social care, zero waste living and the internal revolution of unlearning our internalised sexism, racism, ablism, etc are all vital elements as well.

I can't do anything by half-measures – so I think I'll set up a big commune :-)

A Sense of Place

BILL PHELPS

Do geographical and social location play a part in shaping cohousing communities? What determines whether they are accepted as part of the neighbourhood or seen as an oddball intrusion? Over the last ten years, Chapeltown Cohousing has been trying to address these issues.

Introducing ChaCo

ChaCo is a cohousing project that's been in development for over ten years. It shares a lot of characteristics with other cohousing projects: a blend of privacy and sharing, a commitment to working and living collaboratively, a desire to nurture a sense of community – and a common-house. And like all cohousing projects, it has another set of characteristics that are uniquely its own and give it a distinctive taste.

ChaCo's flavour flows from its location and origins. In 2010 a group of friends had been looking for a more communal way of living when they came across an article in the Guardian about Springhill Cohousing in Stroud. They paid a visit and became convinced that cohousing was what they'd been searching for.

They were also aware that there was another group the other side of Leeds who were well on the way to setting up Lilac Cohousing. But ChaCo's founders didn't want to move over to Bramley: they were already well-rooted in Chapeltown and had been living there for decades. They wanted to strengthen their links with their home community, not tear them up.

Fast forward ten years with a quick change of tense and pronoun. We now have a site, planning permission, funding and a viable business plan to build 29 homes, together with the obligatory common-house set in a large shared garden. As I write this, the

building work is about 50% complete and we're hoping to be able to move into our new homes about a year from now.

ChaCo's plans and values have all been shaped by our amazing neighbourhood, with its rainbow of cultures and ethnicities, its strong sense of identity and its high levels of deprivation. So as well as the usual cohousing drivers of Sharing and Sustainability, our list of values also refers to Diversity, Affordability and Empowerment.

ChaCo is a housing co-operative, with all residents having an equal say and responsibility in all the major decision-making. Some of the properties are fully rented, but the majority are shared ownership, as this was the only way we could raise enough capital to pay for the development costs. However, the co-op retains at least some of the value of every unit, which helps to ensure that they are not sold on to people who are not committed to our values.

Cohousing flavours

Cohousing groups can coalesce around a number of different starting points:

■ a group of like-minded friends all keen to share more of their lives together

■ a general yearning to live more collaboratively with others

■ an unfulfilled dream of getting back to nature and living off the land

■ a desire to model a more environmentally sustainable way of living

■ the outworking of a faith perspective

■ the lack of suitable housing for a particular minority or demographic

■ an attempt to get to know the next door neighbours better.

That last one is maybe the most extreme version of place-based cohousing. You don't build anything, you don't move anywhere – you simply develop your relationship with the neighbours to the stage where you all commit to sharing more of your lives together. This is what is known as retrofit cohousing. Instead of starting a brand new intentional community from scratch, it's a process of building on existing relationships and developing high levels of mutual trust within your own immediate neighbourhood. A great example is N Street Cohousing in Davis, California, which started when a pair of neighbours agreed to take down the fence separating their gardens. A few decades later, most of the rest of the street had joined in and were living as an intentional community.

When the founding members of a group are long-term residents of the same neighbourhood with a strong affinity to the area, they're unlikely to want to move elsewhere to pursue their cohousing dreams. And in many cases these dreams might include the idea of enhancing the area they call home.

This is the essence of place-based cohousing: growing a sharing and mutually supportive community within and for a particular neighbourhood. This strand of cohousing with its emphasis on place is not necessarily 'better' than other strands based on (say) sustainability, identity, or a shared political or religious outlook, but it does have a few inbuilt advantages.

Knowing your place can make things easier

Existing relationships

A major strand of work for any new community-led housing group is building credibility in the minds of local residents, organisations and gatekeepers. This is usually harder for newcomers to the area. Disadvantaged communities are often wary of outsiders arriving with promises of making things better – particularly when there's a collective memory of earlier promises turning sour.

The group that's already grounded in its area, with members who are known as locals and facing many of the same issues as their neighbours will be in a much better position to win their support. And in addition to understanding local issues, group members may already have useful links and relationships with local officials and elected representatives, rather than having to build these from scratch.

A well-defined area for site searching

Searching for a site can be a lot easier if you can establish the outer limits of where you're prepared to live. Admittedly, this could reduce the number of otherwise viable options, but sometimes a walk round the neighbourhood will reveal interesting possibilities that might never turn up via the more conventional channels. And reducing the number of options can often speed up decision-making and encourage innovative solutions to problem sites.

Community pride

Where a cohousing group grows from within a local community, it's possible that the group's plans can genuinely be represented as something that the community itself is doing. Co-opting local pride can boost support from ward councillors and neighbours, particularly during a planning application when it's essential to have the community on side. However, it's a strategy that could backfire unless the group has already built up a good reputa-tion and there's been genuine consultation involving listening to the neighbours.

Selling the vision

One of the first tasks facing the instigators of a new cohousing project is to formulate a vision and then publicise it to poten-tial residents. For recipients to take it seriously, it helps if the aspirations in the vision relate as much as possible to realities on the ground. Talk of shared meals, safe spaces and mutual support will excite some, but most will be also be wanting an idea of who, what, where and when. The group that can answer the where question can probably also answer large chunks of the who question, making it a lot easier for people to understand what's being proposed.

Of course, once a site has been identified – probably a lot later in the process – the vision can be reinforced by architects' sketches. As well as filling in a lot of the physical detail, these also have the effect of making the project seem much more attainable.

there's inevitably a lot of educating, explaining and reassurance needed before people are ready to get involved

There is, however, a possible downside for groups wanting to recruit cohousing members from a specific local community. Cohousing is a concept that's not widely understood in the UK. Even the broader idea of community-led housing – people working together to provide homes for themselves – can sound strange and scary. So with a smaller target population, there's inevitably a lot of educating, explaining and reassurance needed before people are ready to get involved. Other groups can avoid this problem by recruiting members from a much larger area, vastly increasing their chances of finding people who are already fired up about cohousing.

How Chapeltown shapes ChaCo

Enough of the theory: how did these ideas work out in practice for ChaCo? How did our commitment to one particular corner of Leeds affect how the project developed?

Right from the start we realised that if ChaCo was going to work it would need to reflect many of the characteristics of the local area. As an initial group of (mainly) white, middle class, university-educated people who'd made this diverse and high deprivation area our home for decades, we really didn't want ChaCo to end up looking like us. Our vision was for a home-grown community reflecting the make-up of the local population. And from that simple starting point flowed a number of consequences.

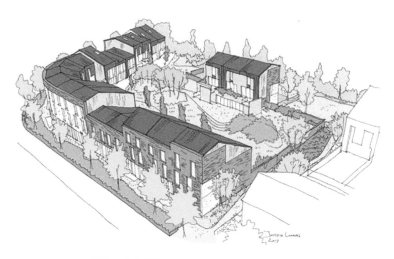

Affordability

Many people in our area have little or no access to capital. At the last census (2011) 55% of households were in some form of social housing, with 17% renting privately.

We didn't want our financial model to exclude those on benefits or those without capital. So the innovative Mutual Home Ownership Scheme being pioneered 5 miles away by Lilac Cohousing just wasn't going to work for us. Instead we decided we would offer rented accommodation at the lowest level we could manage, alongside shared ownership homes to help bring in capital from those able to raise it.

In practice, hard financial realities mean that only nine of our 29 homes will be fully rented – all of them capped at the Leeds Local Housing Allowance level. The rest are shared ownership, with residents owning between 25% and 99%. Consequently, ChaCo owns at least 1% of each of the homes, helping to ensure that the co-operative retains control of its housing stock.

Locals and incomers

In order to ensure that ChaCo remains a genuine home-grown community, our Allocations Policy requires that two-thirds of our members should have a strong pre-existing connection with Chapeltown – and in most cases that means having lived in the area for several years.

Ironically for an area that has been defined, enriched and enhanced by successive waves of immigration over the last century, giving priority to current residents is disturbingly reminiscent of UKIP policy for the nation as a whole. However, Chapeltown has always offered a warm welcome and a home for newcomers, and ChaCo aims to continue this tradition for would-be residents from outside the area. In fact, without a bit of immigration and cross-subsidy from the wealthier areas of Leeds and beyond, ChaCo probably wouldn't be financially viable.

Diversity

For ChaCo, diversity has been one of our core values from the beginning. Partly because we want our community to reflect the area, but more importantly for the richness and expanded understanding that can flow from differing viewpoints. The aspects of diversity that we attempt to monitor and influence through our Allocations Policy include age, income, (dis)ability, identity as LGBT+ and ethnicity.

In every group, of course, diversity can be seen in any number of areas: from education, through personality type, to favourite foods. But In Chapeltown, particularly in the era of Black Lives Matter, diversity is most often associated with race and ethnicity.

Aggregating ethnicity figures from the 2011 Census, the area where the ChaCo homes are being built had a population of 34% African-Caribbean/Black British, 22% Asian/Asian British, 28% Other BME, and just 16% White.

Our strategy is crude but has had at least some success in ensuring that the group becomes less overwhelmingly white. Prospective residents are asked to identify as one of the four

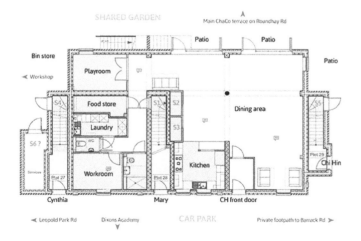

ethnic categories above. Five homes are reserved for each of these groups – and because each group is treated in exactly the same way, we avoid any possibility of discrimination.

The other types of diversity we monitor are treated in similar fashion.

Keeping on keeping on

Our determination to develop a community that's appropriate to this unique area of Leeds has taken us well beyond the existing norms for cohousing in the UK. Those norms reflect a very limited and somewhat privileged section of the population but, if ChaCo succeeds, then maybe we'll have helped the movement become a bit more diverse and inclusive.

Diana Leafe Christian, author of *Creating a Life Together*, and Laird Schaub , a group process consultant, are both experienced and well-respected proponents of community living. They both caution against too much diversity within communities: it's hard enough for a group to work through their differences even when members are from similar backgrounds, so why make it more difficult? ChaCo's answer is (a) that's not our vision and (b) we don't feel that we have much choice. In an increasingly polarised world, we need to develop our CQ – the cultural intelligence that enables us to engage with others very different from ourselves.

Bill Phelps is originally from the South but has lived in the Chapeltown area of Leeds for the last fifty years and is one of the founder members of Chapeltown Cohousing - aka ChaCo.

And because this is Chapeltown, one obvious starting point for many of us in ChaCo is to understand the racism that's shaped all our lives for so long and our own unwitting role in allowing it to persist.

Scribbles from the Shed

DAVID HODGSON

What happens to those living communally during a pandemic? An elder living in a big house intentional community muses on life lived with forty other people during a year of lockdown and social distancing.

November 29th 2020

We are less than one month away from the winter solstice and a little over three weeks into what has now become known as "National Lockdown 2". It began on November 5th in our Big House commune with a splendid socially distanced bonfire at home. We topped the structure with the remnants of Boris the scarecrow, which we had built in the Summer when the Queen and three of her corgis came to judge our lockdown scarecrow building workshop event. The games we play to keep ourselves sane through these trying times.

The demographic in our intentional community has changed since Lockdown 1. During the interim period between lockdowns one and two, where a degree of freedom was allowed, some took the opportunity to leave for foreign lands and some took the opportunity to move in, having been denied the chance by the first lockdown. So now those living here are as follows. Forty one members, four paying guests and ten children, two of which are teenagers. That makes fifty five mouths to feed each day. In a year from now it will have changed again. But then that is the nature of communal living. It's much the same as a normal existence in society outside come to think of it. For in a street of fifty five people there will always be a yearly movement. The only difference between a street and here, is that in this community we all live together, play together, work together and eat together.

All for the benefit of, (as the recent Spitting Image character of Dominic Cummings puts it), 'The Hive'.

At this point you may be wondering what a paying guest is since we have four paying guests at our place as mentioned above. Three of our paying guests are the adult offspring of members returning to the fold for a while and the fourth is the partner of a member who has just moved in on a six month trial. Renewable if the community is happy. No promises. The only difference between a paying guest and a member is one of security and of non involvement in how the place is run. Paying guests, not members, in other communities find themselves in similar circumstances too. At home a paying guest, in every case, is invited to stay by one of the members. They are a personal guest and not a community guest. The member is both responsible for their guests behaviour and for their financial contribution and the member must not go away for any considerable time, like for a holiday, and leave their guest behind without first passing on their responsibility to another willing member.

Boris the scarecrow burned on the November 5th bonfire

And so, in this lockdown there is no more Dominic Cummings to hover around Boris now that he has 'resigned', or been sacked and taken his cardboard box back to Durham. We have a Brexit transition ending that looks like it might be a no deal. We have road haulage companies blocking the roads to the ports as January 2021 approaches. It will only get worse we are told, with food shortages and more food poverty looming. And across the pond, Four Seasons Total Landscaping Ltd are getting unpresidented press coverage for all the wrong reasons, though I hear they are doing a good trade in T-shirts, and an American president is so far up his own backside he's gone blind, along with his drippy sweaty lawyer Rudy "All the Networks, Wow!" Giuliani. All this on top of a global pandemic, a refugee migration that has become increasingly more desperate and dangerous, and a climate emergency that's getting worse by the season and is here to stay. We'll be growing our own root ginger in the years to come, planting olive trees and harvesting more grapes for our home made wine. Chateau plonk.

No wonder, in these unprecedented times, there is an increase in people seeking out alternative ways to bring up their children. Seeking out sustainability, community, family values, co-housing, off grid living, hashtag van life and hashtag tiny house etc. Bring it on. I have always thought that this was the way forward, but I sometimes wonder if it really is? For instance. How many intentional communities are there? How many have fallen by the wayside? How many co-housing schemes have been set up in the past few years? How long does it take to set up such alternatives? And above all. Where are the government incentives and initiatives to help support and finance such alternative economic and ecological ways of living? Where are the collective mortgages, the house sharing insurance schemes and the like? All would help. It has always been said that radical change is needed but nothing much has happened in the past fifty years. Where are the self built housing schemes like the one Walter Segal initiated in Forest Hill back in the 1960's? So few have been built. The status quo remains.

Some 'new seekers' must be kicking themselves for not acting much earlier. Indeed the number of letters of application from potential members that start with words like 'for a long time now we have thought about living in a community' bears witness to this. What is it that motivates people into action these days? Desperation, disillusionment, desire for change, or a combina-

Dave in blossom

tion of all three? When I chose to live this way, more than forty five years ago, I was driven by a desire to live close to the soil, to live an egalitarian way, a green, self sufficient organic low energy way. One that shunned the norms in society. I wanted off the conveyor belt. My dream was that of the Diggers, the Anarcho Syndicalist. Influenced by thinkers and writers like Noam Chomsky, Theodore Roszak, Alan Watts and on the practical side by John and Sally Seymore, Robert and Brenda Vale and the revolutionary urbanism of Street Farm. The latter being a group which I was directly involved with. I sought a work life balance that was both holistic, stress free and nurturing. My friends, my peers, my contemporaries, were all seeking a new way forward for their lives too, as all young people do. Some chose the more spiritual path, I call it the 'Osho' route, while others chose more conventional awakenings. Myself on the other hand chose the intentional community route. Exploring places in the early 1970s like Shrub Family, Biotechnic Research and Development (BRAD) and The Hulk Housing Association, (a twenty seven acre farm in Wales), before eventually settling down here in this big house community some years later.

Kids carrot patches – a lockdown activity

The application process for all potential members wishing to join an existing big house community or co-housing set up is pretty much the same whichever place you are applying to. It hasn't changed much either. Basically you write expressing your interest and explaining who you are and a bit about yourselves. That gets passed around the members and you get invited to visit for a few days. You go away, you write again, you visit again and so begins a cycle until the members are happy with you. Or not as the case might be. If all is well and there happens to be a suitable space available in the community then you are invited to join. The offer is made. This process can take as little as three or four months but equally, and more often, it can take a year or more. I have even heard a member in another community tell a potential member that five years is the process time. After the offer is made then begins the moving in process. Which, in itself, can take up to six months or more depending on your circumstances. There is no quick fix. No bucking the system. Commitment is the word. The long process can be quite harrowing, slow and cumbersome. Some people who embark on this process stumble at the first fallen hurdle and give up. Others persevere and succeed. If you are new to this process then it is always advisable to keep your options open and explore a number of communities. In this way you get to experience and understand the similarities and the differences. You get to weigh up your options, to clarify your needs and understand those of your host. All this takes time and if you are in a hurry, forget it. The added problem in 2020 is that the pandemic has put an abrupt stop to this process in most communities. Numbers contacting communities have trebled but visits have been thwarted. Most communities have closed their doors, to applicants, wwoofers, friends and family. Everything is on hold and has reverted for the time being to the occasional zoom session. Far from satisfactory.

Here is a little story for all you potential members toying with the idea of making a radical life change. A group of new wwoofers joined a work party on their first day to help clear a particularly aukward patch of cooch grass riddled land ready for planting a fresh vegetable plot. It was a day long exercise, a morning session with tea breaks and a similar session post the lunch break. Plenty of time for 'getting to know you' discussion and banter whilst working. At the end of the day all wwoofers bar one were exhausted but satisfied with their work. The one that wasn't, had spent the day leaning on his fork and talking non stop with the group, his patch of ground had barely been touched. As they were all about to finish for the day the one dissatisfied wwoofer stuck his fork in the ground and announced that he was a dreamer and not a digger. He left the next morning having concluded community life was not for him. Too much hard work. Given the choice communities will always go for the Diggers, they are gold dust. Dreamers are two for a penny.

December 15th 2020

In the USA, the Electoral College have today cast their votes and Putin phoned Biden to congratulate him. Trump has still yet to concede and has lost all but one of some thirty lawsuits contesting the election result of November 3rd. Back in Blighty,

Johnson has called out the navy to scare off the French from fishing in 'our waters' while we converge even closer to a no deal scenario. Watch this space. One good thing is that the first vaccine for COVID 19 is being rolled out. Not everyone of course will want to take a vaccine and that must be respected. The choice is a human right after all.

So here we have it. Life on an organic farming intentional community that's been in existence since 1974. A community that is currently negotiating its way through a global pandemic using the process of self management, consensus decision making and regular covid meetings. A community protecting its vulnerable members, the eldest of which is ninety nine, whilst at the same time continuing to run a seventy five acre farm on a self-sufficient basis. It has been a particularly hard year.

Dave Hodgson has done dreaming and now spends most of his time digging with the wind at his back and the sun on his face. A hammer and a saw, a fork or a rake, never far away from his hands.

Me, I'm here in the shed. The shed in my mind. Looking out, digging carrots for the dinner table, pruning fruit trees, wondering when to start that winter carpentry project and watching the world go by from inside my little bubble. Watching the children playing on the roof of the boat, on the trampoline, exploring, adventuring, listening, learning. I love it here. I could not have wished for anything better than to be stuck here throughout a global pandemic. To be stuck outside every day through the seasonal changes, growing my own food, with nothing but space and nature around me. I look forward to the time soon, when family, visitors, wwoofers and pundits grace these beautiful grounds once more and we can welcome visits from potential members again.

Pruned apple trees in the snow

Talking Intentional Community Blues

CHRIS COATES, JAMES DENNIS, JONATHAN HOW AND KIRSTEN STEVENS-WOOD

As nearly six years have passed since our last printed directory, we pondered what had happened to communal living in that time, and where it might be going in the not too distant future.

Kirsten: ...from where I'm sitting, I guess something I definitely think I'm seeing is this drive down the professional recognition road you know there's the Community Homes Grant. There's the big massive, well it feels much more massive and organised, Community Led Housing movement. And I think from my perspective that's a double edged sword. As on the one hand it feels like giving some form of legitimacy and recognition in wider society and then on the other hand I think it loses some of that grounded grassrootsy, chaotic, lovely alternative - the further it's embedded within the society in which we live the less alternative and the less radical it can be. It's the nature of it - if the governments funding it, it isn't going to be radical... and I guess I also find it quite scary that it's a conservative period, politically conservative period that we are finding that this embracing of community led housing is because I think it suits some agenda to push responsibility for housing on to people instead of a social responsibility.

Chris: Linked to that I would say that the whole growth in cohousing is part of that. In that cohousing is about trying to be the acceptable face, if you like, of intentional communities. And largely for people with money. The interesting phenomena there is the number of what you might call 'old school communes' who are busy rebranding themselves as cohousing. Canon Frome, Postlip Hall... all these places that years ago would have had no problem being called a commune and might have even gone "Well intentional community that's a bit vague isn't it?"

James: These are like pre-Housing Co-op places. Places that organised themselves before. They were in a liminal time weren't they of developing.

Chris: ... I've had discussions saying "well they're not really cohousing" They've not got the architectural design element of cohousing. They're living in these big old houses and are actually working against the architecture. And then you've got the Low Impact, or Off-Grid as it's now become basically branded. You hear very few people using the words low impact that was the buzzword when we were producing the book. Simon Fairlie's definition. Off-grid is now the big thing and I look at them and go these often have the same structure as cohousing... The new buzzword are; Off-grid, hubs, cohousing... coliving actually. Coliving is the other word that has come in and is being used for all sorts of purposes.

Kirsten: I keep coming back to this image I saw a long time ago... its where they've made a house out of a metal shipping container and it's got flower pots outside. But it's still a shipping container - and it is saying capitalism will covert almost anything into profit. They'll take something that was an original idea or something that is quite radical and they'll convert it. And I see coliving, which is essentially just flat sharing with a gym and a swimming pool. It's like we could make a lot of money here.

James: That's exactly what it is...

Chris: But it's now also being used in a wider context. I've heard Radical Routes houses being called coliving.

Kirsten: Yeah that's because the term is emerging isn't it. The term itself is emerging. But I also think that there are people out there who are thinking about this as a business model. And think they can now glamorise sharing and appropriate it.

James: I think that's evidence of the thing you were talking about at the beginning Kirsten you know of the mainstream absorbing and regurgitating these things and calling it something else. That's a very marketable term. It's like they've adopted 'Co' as a word to stick in front of things.

Chris: Yeah what we would have called co-operatives in the past has now just got this co word at the front.

Jonathan: ... without the operative bit. To me people place themselves on a spectrum of desire when it comes to involvement in running the thing as well. We are, kind of, all from backgrounds where we assume that that's what everybody wants. But actually a lot of people maybe don't. And, you know, I think as a sixty something man... if I was suddenly made to live in London. Well I think I might sign up to one of those coliving places that were run as businesses. Because (if I could afford it) I'd have the advantages of the shared facilities which feel like a good thing. But I don't think I particularly would want to be involved in running it. So if somebody else wants to run it and make money out of it well fair enough.

James: Or make efforts to actually know the people you are living with and running it with. And have that human thing or not.

Jonathan: .... I mean there could be younger people who join it, and they don't know anything about communes. Or they think they are all weird stuff. And then they read about coliving in some glossy magazine and join it. And then they think "yeah, maybe we could run something like this ourselves".

James: ... I was thinking from a different perspective about people that aren't doing well in this climate and what are they doing in intentional community and co-operative living. And again a thing that has fascinated me for a long time has been like warehouses with demolition orders that you can stay in as a guardian for short lengths of time. And artist communities specially. What I've been interested in is artists communities in London. You know scrabbling around and trying to survive, have a roof over your head and somewhere to work. Generally yeah how people that are more on the breadline or living in relative poverty - how are they dealing with it? What response is coming from that class of people.

James: I suppose I've gotta talk about stats. Cause if were looking back five years at what's happened. We've got to bring up some degree of stats. Can we say anything or represent anything. I suppose we've just got the last book and this book and we can say what's happened. Can we say like what impact did Brexit have on X. You know on intentional communities. We could say well did it have any impact or not.

Chris: I think what the stats might show is that there are a lot more people trying to set places up. Whether there are a lot more places getting set up is another question. Certainly there's a lot more interest.

James: I like that. I like that whole thing about austerity and difficult times being fertile ground for taking more risks.

Chris: We now have over 20,000 members of our Facebook group.

James: That's huge then. Was that in existence five years ago? I dunno.

Jonathan: Yes, I think it was. It started as a Communes Britannica group didn't it? Then was renamed to Diggers & Dreamers. I think it did exist.

Chris: And I would say that social media is a whole new phenomena that's grown in that period. And it's not at all clear what those 20,000 people are really interested in. I mean some of them are desperately looking for somewhere to live. And communities are using it - I don't know how successfully. Communities didn't start using it as a way to recruit, but I would say in the last couple of years they're using it more and more when people know it's there. And maybe that's just communities might be more happy to use social media than they were. You must remember Jonathan we had an article in D&D that basically said that people who were living in communes were Luddites and were actually anti-computers.

James: No! I'm a proud Luddite and I'm not anti-computers. It's about their appropriate use.

Chris: We could dig the article out. Somebody went round and interviewed people in communities.

Jonathan: Yes that's right. I'd forgotten that.

Chris: So the fact that we have now got 20,000 followers on social media is pretty amazing... Not that D&D was ever anti-computer.

Kirsten: I've been reading Andrew Rigby's book, which is a long time ago. So he's writing in the 1970s.

Kirsten: Then you read more in the 1980s and 1990s and as you said Chris there's this emphasis... Like the squatting movement I think was much bigger and the legislation hadn't closed in on people so much I think... And of course that would have an arm that reaches into the future. From my reading of a historical overview there was a real focus on kind of Wholefoods, giving people cheap options for housing and moving from place to place and all of those things. And that we're living in a more regulated space, in some ways, now and that has maybe changed some of the landscape...I think that if you looked at the rationale for why people were coming together, or what a community professed to be their goals I would say there in probably more of a prevalence of the language of climate change. Whereas previously it might of been around self-sufficiency or about providing accessible afford-able homes for people, Or maybe even the political stuff around feminism and what is now Black Lives Matter, multi-culturalism.

Jonathan: I would have said in those earlier decades that survivalism was a very common thread – that's the other side of environmental thing of course. It was much more to do with resource shortage, or anticipated resource shortage then. Now the identified problem is over use of those resources and the unintended consequences of that. The same lifestyle change is the answer to both those problems of course. So it's very easy to flip from one rationale of communal existence to the other.

Chris: In this conversation we also need to mention the pandemic. Because I think that's a factor that has driven people to start thinking about living in a different way.

James: Almost too soon though to really reflect on how...?

Chris: The most common conversation I have with people when they raise it is that I say my observation of what happened here at Forgebank is that we already had all the things in place that people have scrambled to put in place in their street; so we already had a WhatsApp group for our 'street', we were already doing shopping for people who were vulnerable. We already had the social infrastructure to do all these things. There's an interesting dialogue - people go "Oh I hadn't thought about that." We were already a resilient community - we didn't realise it. We were just doing it because it seemed to make sense.

James: Yeah I like that. Resilience. And thinking about people I speak to and how unaffected they are. And actually my life, just my little bit of life got better. I think partly that is because I'd chosen, for its downsides, a resilient path that is much less affected or unaffected by what's going on... with the State and economics - I don't really appear in it.

Jonathan: Have you heard this term 'Islands of Coherence' anybody? I'm not sure who invented it. But somebody was talking about it in a meeting down here a few weeks ago.

Jonathan: It's essentially what you're saying Chris. You know – there might be a cohousing group, a co-op, a social enterprise or something like that. They're doing things already in the way that everyone will do them in the future. But they're kind of viewed as being 'weird' because they're so different from the mainstream. But when the mainstream starts collapsing they then become the islands of coherence around which other things can rebuild. I don't know whether you've ever heard the stuff about how caterpillars turn into butterflies?

Kirsten: They dissolve themselves don't they?

Jonathan: That's right... sort of. I didn't know about it at all until I heard this at a conference at Findhorn at the end of the 1980s. I couldn't believe it really. So once the cocoon is formed the caterpillar dissolves and then rebuilds itself as the butterfly. But apparently the cells that are the basis of the butterfly's wings are already there in the caterpillar. They're sitting there saying "We wanna be wings! We wanna be wings! We don't want to be part of a boring old caterpillar crawling along the ground". But the rest of the caterpillar is saying "F**k Off! We like being part of a caterpillar crawling along the ground. We can't imagine anything else."

Chris: Its basically the quote I keep coming back to... the William Gibson quote isn't it? "The future is already here. It's just not very widely distributed."

Jonathan: That's right. Yeah.

James: God Bless William Gibson!

Directory of Communities in Britain

Since 1990 Diggers & Dreamers has provided the definitive listing of British communities. We are now almost completely web-based but the demand for a printed edition goes on...!

S o you've surfed the websites, read a few articles on cohousing or Off-Grid living and flicked through the directory pages – mentally crossing off half the groups because; they have the wrong diet, do or don't keep animals, are too spiritual or not spiritual enough, appear far to idealistic or too down-to-earth for you taste. What should you do now?

Arranging to Visit

Arranging your first visit to an intentional community may feel like a big deal... Will they like me? Will I like them? Will it be as good as it sounds? What will I have to do? Am I ready for this? Don't fret too much. When you start to read the entries in the directory, you will notice that there is a wide variety of types of communal living groups; some of these groups may work together, some may share income, some may not necessarily live under the same roof; whole groups, or people within the groups, may be committed to ideals such as permaculture, veganism, home education and struggling against sexism, racism and homophobia; others may well not. All the groups in this directory, however, share a desire to be public (to a greater or lesser degree) about their lifestyle.

The reality is that at any one time there are a number of communities actively seeking new members and most groups that advertise themselves welcome visitors and are experienced at hosting all sorts of people. The hardest part may be deciding which group(s) you want to visit in the first place – you can try and find out as much as you can about a place before making your mind up, but the information you get may be sketchy and anyway it can be quite hard to judge a place simply from what they write about themselves. If you can't make up your mind choose two or three that seem close to what you are looking for, or a couple in the area you want to live in. Remember that you will be going into people's homes, and it is important to write to them – letting them know why you are interested in their particular place – then waiting for an invitation to come. Whatever you do, please don't just turn up.

If you are writing to a group whose address you have got from an ad in a magazine or directory, or if you are responding via the group's website getting the balance of your letter, or email, right can be tricky. You don't want to write too much or too little. It is best to try and avoid just writing a long list of questions about the community, and forgetting to include information about who you are and what you're seeking. Whilst there is no formula that will guarantee that your letter will appeal to any particular group, and you should write in whatever your own personal style is, a good aim would be to give equal emphasis to:

- describing what you're looking for, how you heard about them, and why they interest you;

- telling them about your history, skills, and special needs

- and posing questions about the community and how to visit.

Visiting communities can be a bit like dating—people on both sides can have a tendency to put their best foot forward and try to hide what they consider to be weaknesses. You are also unlikely to get to know all aspects of a community on a 'first-date'. Try and be aware of what you may have missed. Did you get to see the group at a meeting? Were there members that you didn't meet? Did you only visit during the week when everyone was working or vice versa?

Making yourself useful on your visit can be done in a whole variety of ways. Pitch in with everyday chores such as gardening, farm work, construction projects, cooking, cleaning, washing dishes, childcare. You may gain "Much Appreciated Guest" status if you have special skills to offer: layout or graphic design , DIY and building skills, computer skills, furniture repairs, storytelling, music, massage........Often, however, the most appreciated contribution is your willingness to pitch in to help with whatever boring chore needs doing at the moment. Though if the group aren't able to involve you in their work and don't have much time to spend with you, be prepared to entertain yourself: take books,

CDs, musical instruments, etc. To dig deeper, learn how to ask friendly but penetrating questions. After you've gotten to know a new group well enough to get more personal, try posing such open-ended queries as:

- What are some of the things you like best about living here? The least?

- What are some of the big challenges your community is facing now?

- How has the community changed over the years? What changes would you like to see in the future?

- What is the procedure for accepting new members?

- How much communal work is expected from members?

- What are the unwritten rules of the community?

- What is the process of decision making on the community?

- How does the community deal with conflict?

- What are the arrangements for leaving the community?

It's probably an excellent idea not to fire off all these questions at once! Most importantly – don't be shy. Groups rely on a stream of visitors to find the new members that are essential for the ongoing life of the community, and a wealth of experiences await you! Good Luck on your communal journey!

How to use the Directory

Over the 30 or so years that we have been producing a directory of communities some have remained remarkably stable, others have changed – with the times, with the people living there. New ones have formed on a regular basis and others have wound up. There are groups listed on our website who didn't want to be in the book and there are also many other communal groups which choose not to be listed at all.

Since our last print outing numbers of communities wishing to be included in this new directory have remained the same. However there has been an exchange of 26 different groups. Only 5 of which no longer appear on our website. This includes 5 new cohousing projects and 6 new housing co-operatives.

Also, just as we announced a steady migration south west last time, this time it appears a steady migration away from names at the beginning of the alphabet towards the end is occurring!

The Index on pages 94 and 95 is intended to help you select the groups you may wish to visit. We have tried, as far as possible, to go by groups' own answers to the questions. A ■ is only shown if their answer was definitely "yes". If their answer was "no" or ambiguous then nothing is shown. In such cases it might mean, for example, that they do share income in some way or that they do eat communally occasionally.

A letter denotes those communities with a spiritual focus:
A Anthroposophy (philosophy of Rudolf Steiner)
B Buddhist
C Christian
Q Quaker
S Spiritual but non-specific

The Icons decoded

Land and Food

 land management programme, members expected to help look after the land

 grow a lot of vegetables – substantial garden (but not necessarily self-sufficient)

 animals reared for food – livestock reared for human consumption

 regular communal meals

Transport

 regular use of bikes for transport

 shared use of vehicles – car pool or recognised arrangements for sharing private cars

 easy access to public transport – bus stop and/or train station within walking distance

Money and Politics

 income sharing community – all income is shared

 capital required – capital required from all members

 community involved in campaigning

Resources

 shared utilities – domestic facilities (eg washing machines) shared

 shared workshop – communal workshop and communally owned tools

 organised recycling system

 eco-friendly sewage system – compost toilets, reed beds, other alternatives in use

 broadband internet access available – possibly networked

Energy Use

 on site electricity generation – wind, water or solar energy provides some power

 solar power used – solar used for space and/or water heating

 insulation to a high standard – buildings are double-glazed and insulated

Smoking and Access

 policy which restricts smoking – smoking restricted to certain areas or banned

 wheelchair access

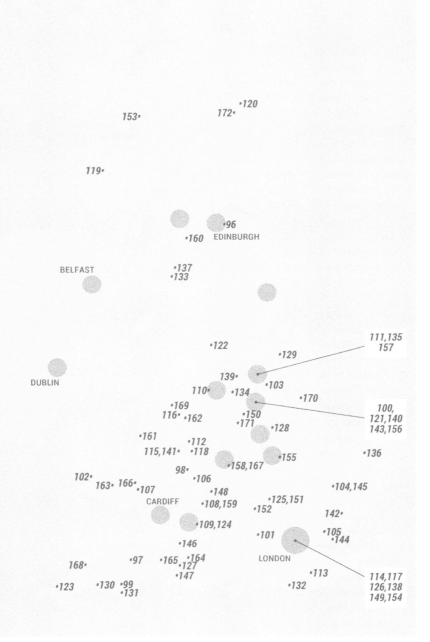

•120

153•   172•

119•

•96

•160   EDINBURGH

BELFAST   •137
               •133

                                              111,135
                          •122   157
                                    •129

DUBLIN   139•
                  110• •134   •103
           •169   •170
      116• •162   •150   100,
                        •171   121,140
   •161   •112   •128   143,156
   115,141• •118
                    •158,167   •155   •136
        98•   •106
102•
   163• 166• •107
          •107   •148   •104,145
      CARDIFF   •108,159   •125,151
                          •152   142•
              •109,124
                    •101   •105
                              •144
           •146
168•   •97   •165 •164   LONDON
              •127   114,117
              •147   •113   126,138
•123   •130 •99   •132   149,154
        •131

	postcode	situation	number of adults	number of children	open to new members	charge visitors	work in lieu possible	daily communal meals	spiritual focus	page
Bath Street	EH15 8GZ	urban	4		■					96
Beech Hill	EX17 6RF	rural	12	5	■	■	■	■		97
Birchwood Hall	WR13 5EZ	rural	11	3	■	■	■	■		98
Bowden House	TQ9 7PW	rural	33	11	■	■	■	■		99
Brambles	S3 9EH	urban	7		■			■		100
Braziers Community	OX10 6AN	rural	14	1	■			■		101
Brithdir Mawr	SA42 0QJ	rural	12	5	■			■		102
Brotherhood Church	WF8 3DF	rural	5		■			■		103
Cambridge Cohousing	CB4 2ZE	urban	70	40	■	■	■	■		104
Cannock Mill	CO2 8YY	urban	30		■					105
Canon Frome Court	HR8 2TD	rural	30	12	■	■	■	■		106
Coed Talyan	SA19 9DR	rural	2	2	■					107
CoFlats Lansdown	GL5 1TN	urban	14		■			■		108
CoFlats Sladbrook	GL5 1TN	urban	14		■			■		108
Cohousing Bristol	BS3 5ES	urban	11		■			■		109
Cordata Co-op	M20 3EA	urban	6		■			■		110
Cornerstone	LS7 3HB	urban	16		■			■		111
Crabapple	SY5 6HA	rural	9	1	■	■		■		112
Darvell Bruderhof	TN32 5DR	rural	180	100	■			■	C	113
Deptford Hsng Co-op	SE8 4LY	urban	80		■					114
Dol-llys Hall	SY18 6JB	rural	9	2	■			■		115
Dragons Co-op	SY10 0JW	rural	3		■		■			116
The Drive	E17 3BW	urban	11		■			■		117
Earthworm	SY7 0LH	rural	12	3	■	■	■	■		118
Erraid Community	PA66 6BN	rural	7		■	■		■	S	119
Ewe House	IV36 3TS	rural	7		■	■	■		S	120
Fireside	S3 9DN	urban	10	3	■			■		121
Forgebank	LA2 6FD	rural	58	13	■			■		122
Friendship Cohousing	TR16 4QZ	rural			■					123
Fruit Corner	BS6 5BU	urban	18	1	■			■	C	124
Giffard Park	MK14 5PA	urban			■	■				125
Guiseppe Conlon	N4 1BG	urban	5		■		■	■	C	126
Hilfield Friary	DT2 7BE	rural	22	4	■			■	C	127
Hockerton Housing	NG25 0QU	rural	10	5	■	■				128
Holy Rood House	Y07 1HX	urban	30		■	■		■	C	129
Keveral Farm	PL13 1PA	rural	11		■	■	■			130
Landmatters	TQ9 7DL	rural	9	7			■	■		131
Laughton Lodge	BN8 6BY	rural	70	36	■	■		■		132
Laurieston Hall	DG7 2NB	rural	19	4	■	■	■			133

	postcode	situation	number of adults	number of children	open to new members	charge visitors	work in lieu possible	wwoof host	daily communal meals	spiritual focus	page
Lifespan	S36 4JG	rural	20	7	■	■	■	■			134
LILAC	LS5 3AG	urban	33	12	■	■	■	■			135
The Loke Community	NR11 8DF	rural	5		■			■			136
Lothlorien	DG7 3DR	rural	21		■	■		■			137
The Nevil Community	N16 8SL	urban	6	2	■	■		■			138
Nutclough	HX7 8HA	rural	7		■	■	■	■			139
Oakleigh	S4 7AG	urban	8		■			■			140
Old Chapel Farm	SY18 6JR	rural	7		■	■	■	■			141
Old Hall Community	CO7 6TG	rural	45	9	■			■	■		142
On the Brink	S11 9BB	urban	20	6	■			■			143
Othona Essex	CM0 7PN	rural	5		■	■	■	■		C	144
Parsonage Farm	CB25	rural	5		■			■			145
Pendragon Community	BA6 8AQ	urban	9	6	■			■			146
Pilsdon Community	DT6 5NZ	rural			■	■	■	■		C	147
Postlip Community	GL54 5AQ	rural	15	12	■			■			148
Quaggy	SE14 6HW	urban	5					■			149
Quaker Community	S33 0DA	rural	9		■	■		■		Q	150
Rainbow	MK13 0DW	urban	31	6	■			■			151
Redfield	MK18 3LZ	rural	10	6	■	■	■	■			152
Rubha Phoil	IV45 8RS	rural	5		■	■	■				153
Sanford	SE14 6NB	urban	119		■						154
Scraptoft	LE5 2FE	urban	5		■			■			155
Share Instead	S7 1DS	urban	5		■	■		■			156
Shirle Hill Cohousing	S11 9DY	urban	17	3				■			157
Skylark	BN2	urban	7		■			■			158
Springhill Cohousing	GL5 1TN	urban	50	32	■	■		■			159
Talamh	ML11 0NJ	rural	6		■		■	■			160
Taliesin	SY20 8JH	rural	3		■			■			161
Taraloka	SY13 2LD	rural	12			■		■		B	162
Temple Druid	SA66 7XS	rural	6	3	■	■	■	■			163
Threshold Centre	SP8 5JQ	rural	18		■	■	■	■			164
Tinker's Bubble	TA14 6TE	rural	10	2	■		■	■			165
Tipi Valley	SA32 7UQ	rural	50	30	■			■			166
Torch Housing Co-op	B18 5NH	urban	9		■		■	■			167
Trelay	EX23 0NJ	rural	22	11	■	■		■			168
Ty Brethyn	LL20 7BS	rural	9	4	■						169
Wellhouse Community	LN7 6TS	urban	4	1	■	■	■	■			170
Wild Peak	DE56 2EF	rural	5	3				■			171
Woodhead Community	IV36 2UE	rural	8		■	■	■	■		S	172

Bath Street Housing Co-op

Greetings from the Bath Street Housing Co-operative. Our spacious 200 year old Georgian house, nestled in the quaint seaside neighbourhood of Portobello, was established as a co-operative in the early 1980s. We maintain a communal spirit, we hold monthly house meetings, and strive to live as sustainably as possible while taking responsibility for the long-term health of the house and the Co-operative. Home-made sourdough bread and cookies are constant features.

Location
9 Bath Street
Portobello
Edinburgh
EH15 1EZ

Electronic Mail
bathstreetcoop@gmail.com

Over 18s
4

Year started
1984

Situation
urban

Ideological focus
ecological, communal, egalitarian

Legal structure
industrial and provident society

Open to new members?
yes

Charge visitors?
no

Work in lieu?
no

We live in a large country house in Mid Devon. Accommodation is both rented and leasehold, in converted outbuildings and in the main house. On our seven acres of land we grow organic fruit and vegetables. We have 2 polytunnels, a paddock, an orchard, a walled garden, a swimming pool, compost toilets and a reed-bed sewage system as well as a wind turbine, solar panels, and a log boiler.

Together we run a low-key course centre and any excess income is used on community projects. We share responsibility for our home and the land on which we live and have a shared meal together in the evening. We participate in the wider community, promoting awareness of everyone's impact on the environment through working closely with the local Climate Action group and holding occasional community open days

Individuals earn incomes in the wider world in education, support work, complementary health, alternative ceremonies, and handyman work. We do not favour dogmatism, judgement or preaching, and aim to care for one another and enjoy life. We tolerate each other's differences and enjoy having visitors and volunteers. Please email for more information.

Beech Hill Community

Location
EX17 6RF

Telephone
01363 877228

Electronic Mail
beechhill@gmail.com

Over 18s
12

Under 18s
5

Year started
1983

Situation
rural

Ideological focus
ecological

Legal structure
industrial and provident society

Open to new members?
yes

Charge visitors?
yes

Work in lieu?
yes

World Wide Web *www.beechhillcommunity.org.uk*

Birchwood Hall Community

Location
Birchwood Hall
Storridge
Malvern
WR13 5EZ

Electronic Mail
info@birchwoodhall.org.uk

Over 18s
11

Under 18s
3

Year started
1970

Situation
rural

Ideological focus
none

Legal structure
co-operative society

Open to new members?
yes

Charge visitors?
yes

Work in lieu?
yes

We live as a communal household (over two buildings) because this meets many of our personal and political needs and beliefs. We do not try to be self-sufficient, although a number of us enjoy growing organic vegetables. We have a broad sympathy for many green and feminist ideas and values, but beyond that baseline we are a fairly varied group. The key to our success and stability is that we like each other!

THE PEOPLE: We span a wide age range, and we enjoy entertaining friends, relatives and other visitors, so the household can sometimes be quite busy! Most community members have some form of paid employment, whether part-time or full-time, and some work from home.

OWNERSHIP: As a housing co-operative, we own our land and buildings as a group, but no individual member has equity in the property. We each pay a weekly rent, partially income-related, that covers most of the household costs. Our aim is that Birchwood is an affordable place for anyone to live.

THE PLACE: Birchwood Hall Community consists of a large Victorian house and a Coach House as living space, with eight acres of grounds (garden, woodland, orchard, volleyball court and outbuildings). We also have a small 20-bed residential centre called "Anybody's Barn", run as a separate charity. Each member is entitled to his or her own room, and we all share a variety of communal spaces. Some members have office or workshop space within the community. Birchwood Hall is on top of a ridge four miles from Malvern. There are lovely views, but limited public transport and lots of hills to bike up, hence most of us drive cars.

DAY-TO-DAY: Because many of us work outside the community and some of us lead very busy lives, members need to be fairly self-reliant. We are good at providing support in time of need – but not necessarily on an everyday basis! We eat our evening meal together every day – a key part of the communal experience – and we make decisions by consensus and discuss current issues at weekly meetings. But the community is not a "project" – it is a home for the members who live here. We have only recently integrated the Coach House within the community, and are in the midst of a project to create more living space there, this is a time of change for us. We are currently assessing how our two buildings will work together in the context of the longer-term future of the community.

World Wide Web *www.birchwoodhall.org.uk*

Bowden House Community is a thriving intentional community which has been established since 2005 one mile from Totnes in rural Devon. We are a group of families and individuals enjoying learning to live consciously together and with our environment. We don't have any ideological or religious focus in common and accept the diversity of backgrounds and beliefs reflected in our members.

Our land includes an orchard, walled garden, large herb and vegetable gardens and 2 polytunnels, newly planted woodland, a tree house, ornamental gardens and lawns. We also share facillities like a wood workshop, community centre, clay pizza oven, tractor, events/workshop spaces etc.

Some of the things which are important to us include: Singing, music, arts and crafts; developing our communication skills with eachother; Collaborating on community projects and the day to day running of things: celebrating and sharing food together; Sustainability, organic gardening, Forest gardening, biodiversity; Deepening our cennection with eachother and the land we live on.

Most of the properties on the grounds are privately owned and lived in by individual/family members of the community. We have also set up a housing co-operative to own the Manor house (pictured) which includes a more communal household as well as some self contained accomodation. Please feel free to contact us to find out more about any aspect of our community.

Bowden House Community

Location
Bowden House
Totnes
TQ9 7PW

Electronic Mail
info@bowdenhouse.co.uk

Over 18s
33

Under 18s
11

Year started
2005

Situation
rural

Ideological focus
"the alchemy of living together"

Open to new members?
yes

Charge visitors?
yes

Work in lieu?
yes

World Wide Web *www.bowdenhouse.co.uk*

Brambles Housing Co-op

Location
80-82 Andover Street
Burngreave
Sheffield
S3 9EH

Electronic Mail
brambles@riseup.net

Over 18s
7

Year started
1992

Situation
urban

Ideological focus
anarchist and ecological

Legal structure
industrial and provident society

Open to new members?
yes

Charge visitors?
no

Work in lieu?
no

Brambles is a Housing Co-operative based in Sheffield that began as a Radical Routes Co-op in 1992. We share two adjacent houses in a vibrantly multicultural but economically poor area of Sheffield called Burngreave. We usually home between 6-9 members, a variety of urban wildlife and act as a stop-off point for many more folk.

We have an amazing 'Permaculture' garden, dubbed 'Paradise in Pitsmoor' by one of our previous members, complete with fruit trees and bushes, vegetable beds, up cycled hot-tub, rainwater harvest system, greenhouse, community workshop, fire pit, frog pond and integrated compost system.

We also have an integrated heating system in one of our houses, which incorporates water heated from solar thermal panel on the roof and the wood-burning stove. In additional to this we have photovoltaic panels on one of the houses, that generate electricity."

The main aim of Brambles is to give its members control over their housing in order to create an affordable, supportive and secure space to live. This enables our members to not simply work for profit but to pursue more creative and socially responsible jobs and activities. Brambles also aims to act as a springboard for social change work – offering a nurturing and energising home space as a foundation for personal inner change and meaningful outer work, which we engage with through political action, mutual aid and our work in various fields such as healthcare and education.

We recognise that we live in a society, which has been negatively shaped by patriarchy and capitalism. We strive to create a world based on fairness, respect and mutual aid. We believe that living communally allows us to share resources, have a lower impact on the environment and try to move away from the individualistic nature of a capitalist society.

Founded in 1950, Braziers is a non-religious community and a college. The main house is Strawberry Hill Gothic in style and is set in 50 acres of unspoilt Oxfordshire countryside. Longer-term residents with a variety of backgrounds and interests live here and, in addition, there are usually three or four foreign students who come to improve their English and help run the house and grounds. We also have WWOOFers and HelpXers.

Braziers is broadly evolutionist in outlook and has a particular interest in group process and group communication. We have paying guests most weekends and are a popular venue for wedding parties, groups and courses such as yoga, meditation, Forest School Camps and the annual Wood Festival, Supernormal and Sacred Arts Camp.

We also run some of our own courses including beekeeping, organic gardening, spinning and community building. Visitors may either stay in the house or opt to camp in the meadows. There are 28 guest bedspaces in the house, but camping allows us to accommodate up to 1000 self catering.

Our cooking has a seasonal, local and organic emphasis, mainly vegetarian dishes are served. Many of the vegetables come from our own organic kitchen garden, our meat is reared on site and served occasionally. Our land management is sympathetic to nature with commitment to sustainable life.

The atmosphere at Braziers is informal, relaxed and supportive. If you would like to know more about Braziers, our courses and events or to find out about hiring Braziers as a venue, please visit our website.

Braziers Community

Location
*Braziers Park, Ipsden
Wallingford OX10 6AN*

Telephone
01491 680221

Electronic Mail
volunteers@braziers.org.uk

Over 18s
14

Under 18s
1

Year started
1950

Situation
rural

Ideological focus
social research and educative sustainability

Legal structure
community benefit society

Open to new members?
yes

Charge visitors?
no

Work in lieu?
yes

World Wide Web *www.braziers.org.uk*

Brithdir Mawr

Location
Ffordd Cilgwyn
Trefdraeth SA42 0QJ

Telephone
01239 820164

Electronic Mail
visit@brithdirmawr.co.uk

As stewards of this 80-acre farm, we try to live our lives working with, rather than against nature : husbanding goats, ducks, chickens and bees in order to provide our own milk, eggs and honey, and producing organic fruit and veg from polytunnels and large gardens. We coppice wood for fuel, bake bread, preserve produce, and use our own materials such as wood and willow for craftwork.

Accommodation is the traditionally built farmhouse and its outbuildings; electricity is supplied by wind, water and solar and we have a couple of green-design buildings. Communal activities include a shared evening meal every week day (mostly vegetarian, but sometimes including meat)and a weekly communal workday including a meeting.

We run courses and occasional camps, and are able to host small gatherings and workshops. Visitors are welcome by prior arrangement. See website or email us for details on volunteering, short or long term, and on info weekends and courses. Languages spoken are English, Welsh, French, German and Spanish. Smoking is restricted to private living spaces, and outside.

Over 18s
12

Under 18s
5

Year started
1994

Situation
rural

Ideological focus
ecological

Legal structure
company limited by guarantee

Open to new members?
yes

Charge visitors?
no

Work in lieu?
yes

World Wide Web *www.brithdirmawr.co.uk*

To make things clear – we are not a brotherhood or a church. We are a small group of people who are aiming to live in a better way, without consumerism and the madness that goes with it, but making use of modern technology in a pragmatic way. Apart from aiming to live in a way that is sustainable and low impact, we feel it is important to work towards putting things right outside of our own immediate surroundings. We involve ourselves in the local community and in wider movements. We would describe ourselves as environmental and pacifist, vegetarian/vegan, with a healthy horror of what is going on in mainstream politics. We are not religious, or conspiracy theorists, or in alignment to any political parties or new age spiritualism. After a history of 100 years of non-violent direct action, we feel there are many issues needing to be addressed to make the world a better place – some are becoming pressingly urgent, like the climate, environmental destruction and the clampdown on human rights, for example.

There is about ten acres of land here. We have composting toilets and are partly off grid. We have some income from activities on the land, and some of us have separate ways of earning a living. Everyone contributes to the upkeep of the place through helping out, and financially if possible according to their means. Visitors are welcome, but we prefer to meet people before they stay if possible. We are open to volunteers, depending on their skills and interests. There is room here for more permanent members, but we need to get to know each other first. We have facilities to host meetings with camping space and some caravans. We do not charge for this, but expect groups to be self-sufficient with food, etc.

Brotherhood Church

Location
Stapleton
Pontefract
WF8 3DF

Telephone
07946 535745

Electronic Mail
*enquiries@
thebrotherhoodchurch.org*

Over 18s
5

Year started
1921

Situation
rural

Ideological focus
environmental pacifist anti-capitalist

Legal structure
none

Open to new members?
yes

Charge visitors?
no

Work in lieu?
yes

World Wide Web *www.thebrotherhoodchurch.org*

Cambridge Cohousing Marmalade Lane

Location
9 Marmalade Lane
Orchard Park
Cambridge
CB4 2ZE

Electronic Mail
*cambridge-k1-info@
googlegroups.com*

As a cohousing development, Marmalade Lane is a real community – a place to know and be friends with your neighbours. And as well as energy-efficient, architect-designed modern homes, residents benefit from extensive shared facilities and a large shared garden. Cohousing is a way of life in which residents not only get to know their neighbours and enjoy a real sense of community, but jointly manage their living environment together. As well as their own private home, each resident household benefits from shared spaces and facilities that enrich the living experience and encourage a more social way of life.

As a cohousing development, Marmalade Lane is the product of an innovative design process in which members of K1 Cohousing, drawn from all ages and backgrounds, have been involved from the outset. All residents are members of Cambridge Cohousing Ltd and contribute to the management of the community. Residents comes from all ages and walks of life and includes families with young children, retired couples and young professionals.

Over 18s
70

Under 18s
40

Year started
2019

Situation
urban

Ideological focus
community

Legal structure
company limited by shares

Open to new members?
yes

Charge visitors?
yes

Work in lieu?
yes

World Wide Web *www.marmaladelane.co.uk*

We are a mutually supportive cohousing group living in our own low energy and environmentally friendly homes with a shared 'common house', land and facilities at Cannock Mill, Colchester. Our website provides information on our community our homes, land and Common House.

We publish 'Cannock Mill News', our email newsletter, so if you are interested you can subscribe via our website. We know our neighbours and look out for each other and have as much privacy or socialising as we want.

We do not have any central religious or social agenda, we are diverse indiviudals who see the benefits of living in an intentional community. We are agreed however that we all aim to lower our carbon footprint as much as possible, and do through energy efficient homes, wanter efficiency, solar power generation, shared facilities and minimising car use. In other words, "living lightly."

We also try to contribute as much as possible to our wider community in Colchester.

Cannock Mill Cohousing

Location
Cannock Mill
Old Heath Road
Colchester
CO2 8YY

Electronic Mail
enquiries@
cannockmillcohousingcolchester.
co.uk

Over 18s
30

Year started
2019

Situation
urban/semi-rural

Ideological focus
good neighbourliness, eco awareness with equality, inclusion, diversity and democracy

Open to new members?
yes

Charge visitors?
no

Work in lieu?
no

World Wide Web *www.cannockmillcohousingcolchester.co.uk*

Canon Frome Court

Location
Ledbury
HR8 2TD

Electronic Mail
*membership@
canonfromecourt.org.uk*

Over 18s
30

Under 18s
12

Year started
1978

Situation
rural

Ideological focus
*Sustainable living around
organic farming, food and
friends*

Legal structure
*industrial and provident
society*

Open to new members?
yes

Charge visitors?
yes

Work in lieu?
yes

We are an intentional community focused around a farming co-operative in rural Herefordshire. We are made up of a main house, stable block and some detached places that provide 20 self-contained living spaces of varying sizes most of which are leasehold but we also support different models including shared ownership and renting. Together we number about 30 adults and a dozen kids that range from babes in arms to wise seventy year olds.

We make our decisions by consensus in our regular meetings, and make much of our food based on our hard labour and good times in the gardens, pollys or fields. We eat together weekly and are fortunate to have the facilities to host public events to share the place with, amongst others, artists, basket weavers, pilates classes and music lovers utilising the various spaces and rooms we share. There are communal workspaces for making do and mend

Our 40 acres mixed farm follows organic principles in raising a variety of animals including dairy and beef cattle, goats, sheep and chickens. The large walled garden produces year-round veg from year round work, with some help from volunteers.

We enjoy the space we have for picnics, parties, (kids) play areas and even a swimming pool and lake. We aim to tread lightly on the earth with our district biomass heating system supplying most of our heat and hot water, PV providing about a third of our electricity requirements and our ever growing car pool minimising our carbon impact further. Canon Fromers like to work, rest and play!

World Wide Web *www.canonfromecourt.org.uk*

Often looking for additional members and further investment in Coed Talylan, a 70 acre woodland on the edge of the Brecon Beacons. We are currently establishing a mushroom cultivation business and Eco/ Natural Buildig School. New members would need to have experience in agroforestry and related activities and be willing to commit to a One Planet Development application for a co-sufficent community farm.

Coed Talyan

Location
Bethlehem, Llandeilo
SA19 9DR

Telephone
07519 830703

Electronic Mail
agroecologicallandinitiative@gmail.com

Over 18s
2

Under 18s
2

Year started
2018

Situation
rural

Ideological focus
agroecology, food sovereignty, agroforestry

Legal structure
co-operative society

Open to new members?
yes

Charge visitors?
no

Work in lieu?
no

World Wide Web *www.coedtalylan.org.uk*

CoFlats Lansdown

CoFlats Sladbrook

Location
Cohousing Company
16 Springhill Cohousing,
Uplands
Stroud GL5 1TN

Telephone
01453 766466

Electronic Mail
info@coflats.com

The Cohousing Company received planning permission in June 2005 for the first CoFlats community. CoFlats is similar to Cohousing but it's just flats. Stroud Coflats has a shared car, an on-site 2KW wind turbine, super-insulation and re-uses an old chapel in the Town Centre.

There is a common house, two garden areas, 20 secure bicycle lockups, 14 flats and studios.

The related Cohousing Company built the first new-build cohousing community in the UK in Stroud (see Springhill Cohousing entry). And the 3rd Cohousing Community in Stroud. CoFlats Sladbrook.

The principles of Cohousing are that decisions are made by consensus, the site is pedestrianised, the common house is used for shared meals and is a communal extension to residents' private living rooms.

Cohousing is the future. Communal when we want it and privacy when we want it.

Details of both CoFlats communities are available from the website.

Over 18s
14

Year started
2006

Situation
urban

Ideological focus
cohousing

Legal structure
company limited by shares

Open to new members?
yes

Charge visitors?
no

Work in lieu?
no

World Wide Web *www.coflats.com*

CoHousing Bristol is a small, urban cohousing project. We are currently in the process of creating a cohousing community on our site, providing socially, environmentally and financially sustainable housing and shared community facilities for our members.

Cohousing Bristol

Our current membership is 8 directors, 4 of whom live in the farmhouse and 3 new directors, who live elsewhere. There is also a changing cohort of twenty-somethings who rent rooms on a shorter term basis, they are encouraged to be involved in the life of the community, but are not part of the main decision making processes. They do add a great deal to the variety and energy of the place.

Building is expected to start May 2020 on 7 housing units for sale to members. We are in the process of allocating these to new members, and we are not looking for any more applicants at this time.

The houses will be 2 or 3 bedroom, and build to passivhaus standards.

There will also be access to shared gardens with bike stores and sheds and facilities in the farmhouse. These are currently a big shared kitchen, a big living room and a flexible room used as an office, for exercise and as an informal guest room.

Some background: CoHousing Bristol is a company limited by guarantee and was originally set up in 2001. The group bid for various properties or parcels of land unsuccessfully before acquiring our current site.

In 2010 we bought a property consisting of a stone-built farmhouse and just under an acre of land. It was in need of extensive renovation, and we moved in in 2011 after working on it for a year.

Location
Lower Knowle Farm
Berrow Walk, Bedminster
Bristol
BS3 5ES

Electronic Mail
dianeholness@msn.com

Over 18s
11

Year started
2001

Situation
urban

Legal structure
company limited by guarantee

Open to new members?
yes

Charge visitors?
no

Work in lieu?
no

World Wide Web *www.lkfcohousing.com/*

Cordata Co-operative

Location
M20 3EA

Electronic Mail
mailcordatacoop@gmail.com

Over 18s
6

Year started
2013

Situation
urban

Legal structure
industrial and provident society

Open to new members?
yes

Charge visitors?
no

Work in lieu?
no

Cordata Co-operative is the first of several new co-operative house projects that enable groups of people to live in a more sustainable way in large urban houses. Cordata co-operative is in Withington in south Manchester. The house is is owned by a secondary co-operative and run by members of the co-operative house, who have complete control over who lives there, how the space is used, what it looks like. This model also allows for a complete low energy refurbishment, so we have fitted solar panels, a complete insulation envelope, rainwater collection, and other energy reducing features.

Current members are a diverse group of people: musician, lecturer, chef, student, dance teacher, freelance film-maker.

Summer 2015: After an intense year of finishing off the internal work on the house and developing our principles, we are now focusing on living together, and supporting other houses using the same model.

We are registered co-operative and we meet about every month to make bigger decisions and develop our group. Some of our principles incllude a commitment to cooking and eating together, managing energy use, and being creative with a small amount of food growing space.

We occasionally have places available in the house and are happy to help other groups who are interested in something similar. You can contact us via email or look for our page on facebook, The Cordata House (co-operative). We are part of a small network of co-operative houses supported by the co-operative living freehold society.

Cornerstone is not so much a community as a collective of people who share the running of a housing co-op, but who have different political perspectives and focuses for their daily lives.

Cornerstone Housing Co-op

Cornerstone has two large Victorian houses in Chapeltown, a culturally diverse part of inner-city Leeds. Both houses need a lot of ongoing maintenance, and have large gardens front and back, which we variously hang out in, tend or leave wild, attracting wildlife and producing some food (herbs, fruit and veg).

One house has space for 7 members, the other for 8, and there are sometimes short and long-term visitors increasing our numbers. Both houses have large cellars which are home to a wide range of projects – bikes, workshops, brewing and Footprint Workers Co-operative (printers).

We have been able to support a variety of other co-operatives to grow and develop within Leeds. There is an emphasis on members being socially active, and are often involved in local and national campaigns on a diverse range of issues with emphasis on consensus and non-hierarchy.

We eat together, run the houses together, and make decisions together. Cornerstone is an active member of Radical Routes, the UK-wide secondary co-op promoting co-operation and working for radical social change.

Location
16 Sholebroke Avenue
Chapeltown
Leeds LS7 3HB

Telephone
0113 262 1534

Electronic Mail
cornerstone@
cornerstonehousing.org.uk

Over 18s
16

Year started
1993

Situation
urban

Ideological focus
multiple/diverse

Legal structure
co-operative society

Open to new members?
yes

Charge visitors?
no

Work in lieu?
no

World Wide Web *www.cornerstonehousing.org.uk*

Crabapple Community

Location
Berrington Hall
Berrington, Shrewsbury
SY5 6HA

Telephone
01743 761418

Electronic Mail
crabapplecom@hotmail.com

Over 18s
9

Under 18s
1

Year started
1975

Situation
rural

Ideological focus
ecological

Legal structure
company limited by guarantee

Open to new members?
yes

Charge visitors?
yes

Work in lieu?
no

rabapple has been at Berrington Hall since 1977. Situated 5 miles from Shrewsbury, the house is set in about 20 acres of woodland, meadows and growing areas, including a 2 acre walled garden, several polytunnels, an orchard, a willow plantation, and herb and flower gardens.

We aim to live as lightly on the earth as possible - regularly reviewing how we can reduce our ecological and carbon footprint. We grow everything organically, with a diversity of approaches and are self sufficient in fresh produce for over half the year, while doing our best to manage the land for the benefit of wildlife. We aim to inspire others and share skills in low-impact living, for example by hosting volunteers. We also aim to contribute to the wider community by using the grounds as a venue for courses and events (eg permaculture, community arts) and by hosting gatherings in our camping fields – including national environmental/peace groups.

Day to day life at Crabapple is varied and includes gardening, preserving food, cooking, cleaning, house maintenance, renovation, wood processing, hedging, mowing, hosting events, admin/finance etc. Members share responsibility for community projects and domestic work, typically contributing two to three days per week.

We're constituted as a fully mutual housing co-op. You don't need capital to join – we are tenants and pay rent. We also pay into a housekeeping kitty which covers food and bills. We share a vegan/vegetarian meal (almost) every evening. We share bathrooms, living rooms and kitchens. There's a small kitchen for those wanting occasional meat/fish meals.

The house is heated for about 5 months a year with a gasifying log boiler and central heating system. Hot water comes from the log boiler, the kitchen range, and a solar thermal system. We also have a 4kW photovoltaic array and several compost toilets.

The Darvell Bruderhof is located in the hills of East Sussex, about one hundred kilometres south of London, near the southern England coastline. The rolling hills that immediately surround Darvell include woods and hedge-lined fields, usually grazed by sheep and cows. On our property you'll find brick apartment buildings and communal buildings including a dining hall, meeting room, kitchen, laundry, school, offices, and factory.

We are part of the Bruderhof movement. Founded in 1920 in Germany, the Bruderhof ("place of brothers" in German) has its roots in the Anabaptist tradition of Europe's Radical Reformation. We practice adult baptism. We are also pacifists and conscientious objectors. While we love our countries and countrymen, our faith transcends political and nationalistic affiliations.

Our life together is founded on Jesus, the Christ and son of God. We are convinced that a life in church community is the greatest service we can offer humanity and the best way we can proclaim Christ. The Bruderhof movement is not a lifestyle choice. It is an answer to Jesus' insistent call to humankind as expressed in the Gospels, especially the Sermon on the Mount. While we follow the communal traditions of the early church, we believe our way of life is a compelling answer to the problems of contemporary society, with its emphasis on wealth and self, and its resulting isolation, conflict, and inequality.

Through community, we have experienced Christ's transforming love. He makes the impossible possible: for ordinary and flawed men and women to live together in forgiveness and mutual trust, as brothers and sisters. It is his Spirit that calls Bruderhof members to a life of love where work, worship, mission, education, and family life are brought together into a single whole.

Darvell Bruderhof

Location
Robertsbridge
TN32 5DR

Telephone
01580 883300

Electronic Mail
darvell@bruderhof.com

Over 18s
180

Under 18s
100

Year started
1920

Situation
rural

Ideological focus
Christian

Legal structure

Open to new members?
yes

Charge visitors?
no

Work in lieu?
no

World Wide Web *www.bruderhof.com*

Deptford Housing Co-operative

Deptford Housing Co-operative was built in 1978 and is a fully mutual ownership co-operative with 138 residencies, mostly for single people in shared houses, but there are also some self contained houses, bedsits and flats. Seven of the properties are leasehold. The co-op has its own office, community centre, shared wireless broadband and computer facilities, car parks and attractive communal gardens.

Located in the north of Lewisham, the co-operative is well placed for travel into central London. Deptford rail and DLR stations are both nearby and many buses pass along the major routes at either end of the nearby High Street. The historic Deptford Market, Greenwich Park and river Thames are all within walking distance.

Deptford Housing Co-operative issues contractual tenancies and accepts direct applications – it keeps its own waiting list and often has availability in its shared accommodation.

DHC was opened with the aim of creating community housing where all residents share the responsibility of its management and organisation. Its street address, Rochdale Way, commemorates the Rochdale Pioneers, a group of ordinary people who founded the world's first co-operative in the North of England in the 19th century.

Are you interested in co-creating a place to live where the values of co-operation, diversity and communication are cultivated?

Are you interested in active participation in another model of living in one of London's more vibrant, culturally diverse neighbourhoods, independent of the exorbitant property market?

Then come to us.

Location
16 Rochdale Way
Deptford
London
SE8 4LY

Electronic Mail
dhcmne@gmail.com

Over 18s
80

Year started
1978

Situation
urbanl

Legal structure
industrial and provident society

Open to new members?
yes

Charge visitors?
no

Work in lieu?
no

World Wide Web *www.coophomes.coop/client-co-ops/deptford-housing-co-op/*

Dôl-Llys Housing Ltd was formed in 1992 by 6 families as a housing co-operative. It was originally a regency country house but then empty and owned by Powys County Council. The house is divided into 7 private, self contained flats of varying size, one of which is rented. We also have some communal rooms in the house and share all the outdoor space. New members buy into the co-operative through purchasing loan stock giving them a 1/6th ownership of the entire property and grounds. Daily life at Dôl-Llys is more in line with co-housing. A key difference is that we are not an "intentional community" in the general ideological sense. We have different outlooks and lifetyles; our focus is mainly practical and is centred on sharing and caring for communal space, green space and some material resources. We share workloads equitably and this means we can all enjoy and benefit from sharing the house and gardens. By meeting, working co-operatively and eating together each month we are able to build friendly neighbourly relationships. If you are interested in living at Dôl-Llys, please contact the Membership Secretary via the Dôl-Llys website or by email membership@dol-llys.co.uk for the latest information on the availability of shares. For more information please follow the link to our web site. Our vision – Dôl Llys Hall is a co-operative and co-housing community which has at its core the provision of homes for its members. In achieving this, we aim to preserve and enhance the building and grounds and aspire to be low impact and respectful of the natural environment. We wish to be open and welcoming, and to engage with the local community, making the best use of the resources we have available. And to leave it a better place for those who follow.

Dol-Llys Hall

Location
Dol llys Hall
Llanidloes
SY18 6JB

Electronic Mail
info@dol-llys.co.uk

Over 18s
9

Under 18s
2

Year started
1992

Situation
semi-rural

Ideological focus
environmentally aware

Legal structure
company limited by shares

Open to new members?
yes

Charge visitors?
no

Work in lieu?
no

World Wide Web *www.dol-llys.co.uk*

Dragons Co-op

Dragons housing co-operative limited was established in May 2015 and we purchased our first and so far only property in August of the same year. As a fully mutual par value housing co-op we are managed by those tenants who are resident and paying rent.

We were established using the Radical Routes model rules which we obtained via Catalyst Collective. We are also governed by the ethics and principles of permaculture design and the 7 principles of co-operation as set out by the Rochdale pioneers. Dragons is inspired by the work of Robert Owen and the co-operative movement worldwide.

Location
Haulfre
Llanrhaeadr Ym Mochnant
Oswestry
SY10 0JW

Telephone
07719 818959

Electronic Mail
steve@sector39.co.uk

Over 18s
3

Year started
2015

Situation
village

Ideological focus
permaculture, co-operative

Legal structure
industrial and provident society

Open to new members?
yes

Charge visitors?
no

Work in lieu?
yes

World Wide Web *www.dragons.cymru/news-and-updates*

The Drive Housing Co-op owns 8 The Drive, Walthamstow. This is a 11-bedroom former childrens' home, a detached house within a reasonably sized plot of land (for London).

In summary there are three aspects to this project:

– a housing co-op, which enables its members to have a say in the running of the accommodation that they live in, with no external landlord to have to deal with. For us, making decisions by consensus is at the heart of this.

– an intentional community, where people live together as one household, and experiment with new ways of living more sustainably together, within the context of a city and urban lifestyle. This encompasses bulk-buying of food, sharing facilities, and pooling resources in many other ways; acting as a community by providing care and social contact for one another within the house, but also engaging with the local neighbourhood through community events (in the house, garden, or elsewhere), and other involvements.

– a permaculture garden, which will enable us to produce a proportion of our food on-site, reducing food miles and our living costs.

The longer-term aim is that The Drive will act as a living and working demonstration that a group of people can live together in an organised and sustainable way, which moves beyond the normal house/flat-share situation that many single people typically find themselves in.

The Drive Housing Co-op

Location
8 The Drive
Walthamstow
London
E17 3BW

Electronic Mail
enquiries@thedrive.coop

Over 18s
11

Year started
2010

Situation
urban

Legal structure
industrial and provident society

Open to new members?
yes

Charge visitors?
no

Work in lieu?
no

World Wide Web *www.thedrive.coop*

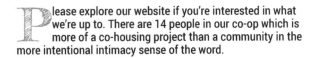

Earthworm Housing Co-op

Location
*Wheatstone House
Dark Lane, Leintwardine
Craven Arms SY7 0LH*

Telephone
01547 540461

Electronic Mail
*earthwormcooperative
@yahoo.co.uk*

Over 18s
12

Under 18s
3

Year started
1989

Situation
village

Ideological focus
hard graft, diverse...

Legal structure
industrial & provident society

Open to new members?
yes

Charge visitors?
yes

Work in lieu?
yes

Please explore our website if you're interested in what we're up to. There are 14 people in our co-op which is more of a co-housing project than a community in the more intentional intimacy sense of the word.

Being a co-op means we all take decisions on the running of the project together, all pay rent and all join in a certain amount of admin and renovation work.

The co-op has seven acres including orchards, kitchen garden, woodland, lounging lawns and a wetland designed by J Abraham that manages all of our sewage and waste water.

There are three buildings made of up three flats, a small house, a 6-person shared house set-up and lots of large communal rooms. We are focused on renovation more than land management for the foreseeable future (2015-2019).

We are not a food/land based project at present, so it isn't appropriate to take wwooFers. We do sometimes have work weeks on renovation and maintenance of the buildings though; please e-mail us with Volunteer in the subject for more information.

We see our focus as being diverse but involving permaculture and a lot of very hard graft!

World Wide Web *www.earthwormhousingcooperative.org.uk/*

Erraid is a small Hebridean island in Scotland, in view of Iona. The island is one square mile in size and our small community lives and works on the land. We live in old light house keepers' cottages, which we share with our guests. Life on Erraid seems pretty much like it must have been in the 1870s when the houses were established.

We work in the gardens, heat the cottages and our water with woodburning stoves, drink rain water and live a life very close to the elements. What we are doing on a day to day basis is often determined by the sea, the tides, the moon and the wind.

One of our main purposes on the island is to hold guests in the island's ancient energy and allow them to experience and explore its magnificent landscape and wildlife, our unique lifestyle and community life. Guests come throughout the year for a week or even months to live with us and join in our activities: cooking, chopping wood, working in the gardens, helping with the animals, making candles, meditating and singing sacred songs in our beautiful sanctuary and celebrating the turning of the seasons in our Celtic Festival weeks. Please visit our website for more information.

Isle of Erraid Community

Location
Findhorn Foundation
Isle of Erraid
Fionnphort
Isle of Mull PA66 6BN

Telephone
01681 700384

Electronic Mail
erraid@live.co.uk

Over 18s
7

Year started
1978

Situation
rural inshore island

Ideological focus
sustainable-spiritual

Legal structure
registered charity

Open to new members?
yes

Charge visitors?
yes

Work in lieu?
no

World Wide Web *www.erraid.com*

Ewe House

Location
Ewe House
Whiteinch smallholdings
Forres
IV36 3TS

Electronic Mail
trschei@gmail.com

Over 18s
7

Year started
2017

Situation
rural

Ideological focus
sharing the Findhorn
Foundation ethos

Legal structure
private ownership

Open to new members?
yes

Charge visitors?
yes

Work in lieu?
yes

The Ewe house – Community within community. Located in Kinloss, Morayshire, Scotland. Our roots are from the Findhorn Foundation (check their web page) and we are part of the wider Findhorn community counting more than 400 people from all over the world. It is simply a privilege to live in rural Scotland in the middle of an international community based on deep social values. There is app. 2000 incoming guests a year – generating many opportunities for participating in workshops and activities. Furthermore, we are in the "Kinloss gap", one of the 3 driest most sunny places in GB. (Not equally happy to have two RAF bases in the vicinity..). The Findhorn Village is an attractive holiday resort worth a visit in itself. We are a 5 acres permaculture based self-sufficiency smallholding, with a large modern 5 bedroom, 4 bathroom house and outbuildings; a venue space and wood-workshop. We have 2 dogs, chickens, some sheep, a fruit orchard, greenhouse and vegetable garden. We define ourselves as a one household, spiritual community sharing the Findhorn Foundation ethos. Our shrine room gives us the space to share 20 minutes of meditation in the mornings, and can serve those that seek "time out of time". An art space and a writers retreat are next steps. Are you an emphat, deep thinker and able to cultivate gratitude? Our land and buildings are well suited for work-shops and therapy work if that is your flow. We are open to flexible, humoros, good workers that are open to some self-critizism. We welcome one or two volunteers or potential new members. If interested please send us a presentation of yourself. Thanks.

Fireside has a row of five mid-terrace Victorian houses in Burngreave, Sheffield. We've knocked our long and skinny gardens into one, giving us plenty of room to play, grow organic veg, have bonfires and parties. There's lots of green space and wildlife around, a shared allotment, a tree swing and an adventure playground at the end of the road.

Burngreave is a quite deprived inner-city area but very multicultural and vibrant. Every adult tenant is a full and equal member, and between us we manage the business and maintain the houses and gardens. The houses are owned by the Co-op, not by the individuals here – but as Co-op members we are both tenants and our own landlords, which gives us greater control over our housing.

Our aims are to provide and maintain affordable good quality housing; to improve the energy-efficiency of the houses and minimise our impact on the environment; and to support and promote the Co-operative housing sector. With two growing families in the co-op we live mostly as five separate households, but we have knocked a connecting door between number 55 & 57 and numbers 59 & 61 have a shared kitchen area. We eat communally on a regular basis, after meetings, and on a Co-op weekend when we work together on the houses and gardens.

We've got PV panels on all roofs and solar hot water in 4 of the houses; we have created large, light, highly insulated kitchens and aim to bring the rest of the structure up to the same standard of comfort and energy efficiency. There is a lot of work in running a co-op, and we welcome applicants with skills such as accountancy, carpentry and plumbing. We often have space for more members, so do get in touch!

Fireside Housing Co-op

Location
61 Melrose Road
Sheffield
S3 9DN

Electronic Mail
fireside@
blueyonder.co.uk

Over 18s
10

Under 18s
3

Year started
1996

Situation
urban

Ideological focus
low cost high quality living

Legal structure
industrial and provident society

Open to new members?
yes

Charge visitors?
no

Work in lieu?
no

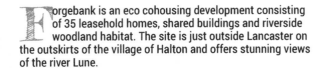

Forgebank

Forgebank is an eco cohousing development consisting of 35 leasehold homes, shared buildings and riverside woodland habitat. The site is just outside Lancaster on the outskirts of the village of Halton and offers stunning views of the river Lune.

We aspire to be a cutting edge example of sustainable 'eco' design, for both living and working, with close links to the local community. The homes have achieved both Passivhaus and Code for Sustainable Homes level 6 certifications, and we benefit from many eco technologies such as heating from a central biomass/ solar system, and electricity from solar PV panels and a mini-hydro plant.

Location
*9 Forgebank Walk, Halton
Lancaster LA2 6FD*

Telephone
07825 610342

Electronic Mail
*info@
lancastercohousing.org.uk*

The project was planned and designed by the residents with architects Eco Arc and local building firm Whittles Construction. Residents, who are members of the management company – Lancaster Cohousing Ltd – actively participate in the day to day running of the community. Discussions are democratic and consensual. While we do have community agreements and policies, our ambition is to rely on trust, respect, friendship and understanding rather than rules and regulations.

Over 18s
58

Our Common House contains a communal kitchen and dining room where we cook vegan and vegetarian meals for each other several times a week. There are communal food stores, play areas, guest rooms, a bike shed and laundry.

Under 18s
13

We also operate a car club/ car sharing system.

Year started
2012

Situation
urban/rural edge

Ideological focus
sustainable living

Legal structure
company limited by guarantee

Open to new members?
yes

Charge visitors?
no

Work in lieu?
no

World Wide Web *www.lancastercohousing.org.uk*

We purchased a property, Maningham, in March 2021 and have transformed it into the Friendship Cohousing Community – a perfect place to live as life becomes more difficult in this uncertain world. This property has private units and a large house with lovely communal spaces. There is an amazing 4-acre garden where we care for the beautiful plants already there and are developing a forest garden and small-holding to grow our own food in harmony with Nature. We wish to help people with information about developing cohousing communities (especially in Cornwall) self-sufficiency, permaculture, rewilding, regenerative agriculture, herbal medicine, deep adaptation & spiritual awareness.

Maningham is close to the village of Illogan, to Tehidy Country Park and to the sea at Portreath, a beautiful Cornish beach with a walk down through the woods.

We plan to have regular open days and spiritual retreats.

Contact us via our website if you'd like to find out about living in this community or visiting Maningham.

Friendship Cohousing

Location
TR16 4QZ

Electronic Mail
jackie@friendshipcohousing.org.uk

Year started
2021

Situation
rural

Ideological focus
cohousing community for the climate crisis

Open to new members?
yes

Work in lieu?
no

World Wide Web *www.friendshipcohousing.org.uk*

Fruit Corner

Location
*10 Cotham Park
Bristol BS6 6BU*

Telephone
0117 924 1241

Electronic Mail
communitylife@lovebristol.org

Over 18s
15
Under 18s
1

Year started
2000

Situation
urban

Ideological focus
*Intentional Christian
Community*

Legal structure
registered charity

Open to new members?
yes

Charge visitors?
no

Work in lieu?
no

"Lord grant that I may seek to comfort than to be comforted; to understand than to be understood; to love than to be loved; for it is by forgetting self that one finds; it is by dying that one awakens to eternal life. Amen"

(St Francis of Assisi)

For us living in an Intentional Christian community is not only a great opportunity but in many ways life changing. Our ideal is that over a period of time the ryhthm of giving and receiving evident in community life inspires in people a more selfless existence, one where life is not so much 'me' focussed, more outward looking.

We also hope to foster an accountibility with each other that facilitates continuing positive change. We want people to leave community life with more love than they arrived with and more able to give that love away.

There are 15 of us living here at Fruit Corner and whilst the turnover of community members is not frequent we do have members that move on from time to time. We are also part of an informal network in central Bristol of 12 other Christian community houses.

If you are interested in this pilgrimage please get in touch.

"Do not be anxious about anything, but in every situation, by prayer and petition, with thanksgiving, present your requests to God. And may the peace of God, which transcends all understanding, guard your hearts and your minds in Christ Jesus."

World Wide Web *www.lovebristol.org/community-houses*

G iffard Park Housing Co-operative is entirely dependent on our own members for income and management and that is the responsibility you take on when you become a member.

Members of a Co-op need to have a genuine desire to have control over their own housing environment, along with a willingness to become involved and take on some of the day to day responsibilities.

Giffard Park Housing Co-op

Location
*Amenity Building
Hainault Avenue
Giffard Park
Milton Keynes
MK14 5PA*

Telephone
01908 618082

Electronic Mail
*giffardparkhousing
@gmail.com*

Year started
1984

Situation
urban

Legal structure
industrial and provident society

Open to new members?
yes

Charge visitors?
yes

Work in lieu?
no

Guiseppe Conlon House

We are a community of the radical Christian "Catholic Worker" movement. The Catholic Worker is an ecumenical, pacifist, and anarchist movement founded by Dorothy Day and Peter Maurin in New York in 1933.

As a community we are dedicated to living simply, in solidarity with those who are marginalised by society and in resistance to violence and injustice.

Location
49 Mattison Road
London
N4 1BG

Telephone
020 8348 8212

Electronic Mail
londoncatholicworker
@yahoo.co.uk

The London Catholic Worker was brought together by the Jubilee Ploughshares 2000 disarmament action, in response to the need for a Catholic Worker community of hospitality and resistance in the world's second imperial city. In June 2010 the London Catholic Worker opened Guiseppe Conlon House. At Guiseppe Conlon House we provide hospitality for destitute refugees and asylum seekers. We have a community meal every evening and other activities such as prayer, bible study and "round table discussions" which are open to all living in the house as well as friends, volunteers and visitors. We also run the Urban Table soup kitchen in Hackney every other Sunday.

As part of our work of resistance we organise vigils and are involved in campaigns against war, arms trade, drones, and in solidarity with migrants and refugees. We take as our manifesto the Gospels, the lives of the saints, especially our CW founders Dorothy Day and Peter Maurin, and the CW "Aims and Means"*. Our aim is "to build a new society in the shell of the old", "a society where it is easier to be good", bringing about a non-violent revolution by changing the world one heart at a time.

*www.catholicworker.org/aimsandmeanstext.cfm?Number=5

Over 18s
5

Year started
2010

Situation
urban

Ideological focus
ecumenical Catholic anarchist pacifist

Legal structure
none

Open to new members?
yes

Charge visitors?
no

Work in lieu?
yes

World Wide Web *www.londoncatholicworker.org*

Franciscan brothers first arrived here in 1921 to establish a home of refuge and rehabilitation for the large number of displaced men who were then tramping the roads of rural England. At the Friary they found a welcome as brothers, the restoration of their dignity through shared work, and the opportunity of rehabilitation and training. From this small beginning has grown the Society of St Francis, an Anglican order of men and women inspired by the example of Francis of Assisi; SSF now has communities of brothers and sisters, and many lay or 'tertiary' members, throughout the world.

Today at Hilfield Friary there continue to live the Franciscan brothers of SSF, but they are now joined by other men and women – young and old, married and single – who together constitute the Hilfield Friary Community. This Community shares in a rhythm of daily prayer, helps to look after the Friary land and buildings, and offers hospitality to guests and visitors. People of all backgrounds are welcome here – Christians, those of other faiths and of none – for rest, retreat, and renewal of life. The emergency provision for 'wayfarers' ended in 2004, but the Friary still provides a place of acceptance and supported living for those who are in particular need.

Following the example of Francis of Assisi there is a particular emphasis on living simply, generously and joyfully on God's earth. The land and the animals it supports are cared for and provide food for the community. There is a common table around which the Community and its guests share meals, and yet there is also time and space to be quiet and alone. The Friary is not just a beautiful, peaceful oasis; the Community has a concern for promoting justice and reconciliation in a troubled world, and for proclaiming a wise ecology in the face of our culture's environmental foolishness.

At the heart of the Friary lies the Chapel where the Community comes together for prayer four times a day. Celebrating the Eucharist and praying the scriptures in the Daily Office, as well as the times of silent meditation, bring us back to the source and goal of all creation, renew us in the life of Jesus Christ, and unite us with our brothers and sisters throughout the world.

Hilfield Friary

Location
The Friary, Hilfield Dorchester DT2 7BE

Telephone
01300 341345

Electronic Mail
hilfieldssf @franciscans.org.uk

Over 18s
22

Under 18s
4

Year started
1921

Situation
rural

Ideological focus
christian (anglican)

Legal structure
registered charity

Open to new members?
yes

Charge visitors?
no

Work in lieu?
no

World Wide Web *www.*

Hockerton Housing Project

Location
The Watershed, Gables Drive, Hockerton NG25 0QU

Telephone
01636 816902

Electronic Mail
contact@ hockertonhousingproject.org.uk

Over 18s
10

Under 18s
5

Year started
1995

Situation
rural

Ideological focus
none

Legal structure
company limited by guarantee

Open to new members?
yes

Charge visitors?
yes

Work in lieu?
no

Hockerton Housing Project (HHP) is a community of five sustainable homes, with a co-operative business on-site running a range of educational and advisory services in sustainable buildings and lifestyles.

Hockerton's earth-sheltered homes were built in the late 1990s with high thermal mass and high levels of insulation to eliminate the need for heating systems. Their innovative design has proven itself, as the homes use 20% of the average UK home's energy use, but still keep cool in summer and warm in winter. Onsite wind turbines and solar PV panels generate their own clean energy to meet much of the homes' remaining energy needs.

The co-housing approach, where individual homes are private, but land, water and energy systems are shared, enables residents to do more with less. It also encourages social interaction and skills which can be lost in more insular housing developments.

– Food is grown communally, with households growing 50 – 80 per cent of their fruit and vegetable
– Chickens provide eggs for residents, bees pollinate the orchard and provide honey, and sheep are kept for grazing and meat
– The 15 acre site provides food, renewable energy and a water catchment area, but also offers space for social activities with a woodland walk, a lake and a football/volleyball pitch
– Residents pay for their energy proportionate to their use, and any income from exported energy and the Feed in Tariff is shared equally.

Each household contributes 300 hours a year to food-growing, land maintenance and managing water and energy systems, with tasks agreed in line with interests, ability and availability.

HHP runs a a not-for-profit co-operative which hosts tours and courses for all ages (see website for details), and provides consultancy services to help others deliver sustainability in their home, community or workplace. The original planning permission required the Project to generate employment, and it provides income and flexible employment for each of the households with jobs following members' interests, skills and availability provided they fall within the broad remit of promoting sustainable living.

World Wide Web *www.hockertonhousingproject.org.uk/*

A place of peace and tranquillity, overlooking the Hambledon Hills, the Centre for Health and Pastoral Care offers therapeutic and safe space for people of all ages. Discovering acceptance and a relaxed environment, guests find empowerment to work towards their own health and well being, with professional support from counsellors, psychotherapists, masseurs and creative arts therapists. The friendship and care of staff and the residential community, excellent home cooking, gardens and animals, laughter and sharing, create a sense of belonging, and a few days or a couple of weeks becomes an important oasis in life for many people.

The gentle Christian ethos of this open, radical community offers a space for guests to develop their own journey in a way that is right for them. Celebrating spiritual diversity, the community reflects theologically through research, accredited modular work and conferences arranged through The Centre for The Study of Theology and Health, an offshoot of Holy Rood House. Whatever draws you to Holy Rood House, as an individual or as a group, you will be sure to find it a special place, and we can be sure that our lives will be enriched by your visit.

Holy Rood House

Location
*10 Sowerby Road
Sowerby, Thirsk
YO7 1HX*

Telephone
01845 522580

Electronic Mail
*enquiries
@holyroodhouse.org.uk*

Over 18s
30

Year started
1993

Situation
rural/ market town

Ideological focus
Christian; radical, inclusive and open

Legal structure
company limited by guarantee

Open to new members?
yes

Charge visitors?
yes

Work in lieu?
no

World Wide Web *www.holyroodhouse.org.uk*

Keveral Farm Community

Keveral Farm has been a community since 1973. We live in a farmhouse, a barn conversion, an extended static caravan, and 3 other static caravans. These, together with our farm buildings, are owned and managed by our housing co-op, One Community. Members should attend monthly community meetings, and do at least 2 hours voluntary work per week, maintaining and improving the house, buildings and land.

The 30 acres of land consists of veg plots, polytunnels, soft fruit, orchard, woodland, meadow and camping. The land has been certified organic by the Soil Association for more than 30 years.

Our worker's co-op, Keveral Farmers, oversees the management of the land. Most members rent areas of the land or buildings to pursue their own projects or commercial activities, which include vegetables, salads, soft fruit, woodland management and firewood, and managing a campsite.

We have done weekly veg box deliveries to local people since 1997. We have a Visitor's Barn which is used for yoga, table tennis, events and group visits. We host WWOOFers and working visitors by arrangement. Further information on Keveral Farm is available on our website.

Location
Keveral Farm
Looe
PL13 1PA

Electronic Mail
keveralfarm@yahoo.co.uk

Over 18s
11

Year started
1973

Situation
rural

Legal structure
industrial and provident society

Open to new members?
yes

Charge visitors?
yes

Work in lieu?
yes

World Wide Web *www.keveral.org*

Landmatters is a rural permaculture co-operative in South Devon, living on 42 acres of pasture and semi-natural ancient woodland, with some naturally regenerating scrub and ancient hedgerows.

The land is stewarded by 10 adults and 7 children living in low-impact structures, mostly benders and yurts, and is totally off-grid. We grow some food (hope to grow more!), keep horses, hens and ducks, manage the woodlands, work communally, run educational events, car share, and use consensus decision-making and Way of Council, with the aim of creating a thriving, ecological community.

We are a Permaculture Association LAND demonstration site and a member of the WWOOF network. Visitor accommodation is usually camping with use of the communal kitchen. We celebrated our tenth anniversary in May 2013, and occassionally have spaces for new members to join us. For more info check out www.landmatters.org.uk

Landmatters Permaculture Community

Location
TQ9 7DL

Telephone
01803 712718

Electronic Mail
landmatters @googlemail.com

Over 18s
9

Under 18s
7

Year started
2003

Situation
rural

Ideological focus
permaculture, low impact, nature connection, education

Legal structure
industrial and provident society

Open to new members?
no

Charge visitors?
no

Work in lieu?
yes

World Wide Web *www.landmatters.org.uk*

Laughton Lodge

Laughton Lodge is a co-housing community set up as a non-profit company limited by guarantee, where all lease holders are directors of the company.

We are 70 adults and children, living in 21 houses and sharing 23 acres of fabulous Sussex meadowland – once a rural, residential hospital. Homes come in all shapes and sizes and are held on a 9999 year lease. We also have 11,000 square feet of communal space in the form of a community centre for our own use and for occasional and regular rental.

The community centre comprises offices, large hall, training room, sun lounge, music room, games and playrooms, dining and cooking facilities and guest rooms. We share the land and our expertise, whether it be DIY, gardening, IT, cooking skills, events organising, animal care, yoga, or car sharing; and much more. We also welcome volunteers on our monthly busy weekends to help with indoor and outdoor maintenance tasks and project work.

Members are involved in a range of trades, professions, businesses or creative industries and are employed and self employed or parenting at home. The age of residents currently ranges from babies to those in their 7th and 8th decades. A generation of children has grown up and moved away since we began, and now there is a new generation of youngsters building dens and rampaging in the undergrowth.

Location
BN8 6BY

Telephone
07714 660887

Electronic Mail
*steve.anderson.hoare
@gmail.com*

Over 18s
70

Under 18s
36

Year started
1998

Situation
rural

Legal structure
company limited by guarantee

Open to new members?
yes

Charge visitors?
yes

Work in lieu?
no

World Wide Web *www.laughtonlodge.org*

Laurieston Hall began as a commune in 1972. In 1987 it transformed itself into a Housing Co-operative, currently home to 19 members, 4 children aged 5-10, and a few long-stay visitors. We live in and around a huge Victorian main house, with a large organic walled garden, surrounded by 180 acres of beautiful woods, pastures and wetlands, stretching from a loch to the north, to the best wee sledging hill in Galloway to the south.

Living spaces use wood for heating and cooking. A hydro supplies much of our electricity. We grow as much fruit and vegetables as we can, keep cows, pigs, hens and bees, and do most of our own maintenance. All of us pay a large portion of our rent in unwaged labour for the co-op. This means ideally spending about two and a half days a week doing what we call "workshare".

Issues that affect everybody come to a weekly co-op meeting in which decisions are made by consensus. Work areas are organised within smaller groups. Co-operation is our common ideology; under that umbrella we lean this way and that, are generally better at dealing with tomorrow than next year, are supportive of each other as individuals as well as co-op members – and we try to have a good time! For more information or to subscribe to our mailing list.

Laurieston Hall

Location
*Laurieston
Castle Douglas
DG7 2NB*

Electronic Mail
enquirylh@gmail.com

Over 18s
19

Under 18s
4

Year started
1972

Situation
rural

Ideological focus
co-operative

Legal structure
industrial and provident society

Open to new members?
yes

Charge visitors?
yes

Work in lieu?
yes

World Wide Web *www.lauriestonhall.org.uk*

Lifespan Community Collective

Lifespan Community Collective (aka Townhead Collective) is made up of around 15 adults and 3 kids.

We have 19 old railway cottages on 3 acres of land in rural Yorkshire.

Lifespan was formed in the early seventies as a rural community and has been through different stages of communal living.

At present, it is a housing co-op whose main aim is to provide housing for its members.

Location
S36 4JG

Telephone
01226 762359

Electronic Mail
*lifespancommunitycollective
@yahoo.co.uk*

We have our own personal space, as well as communal areas comprising of rooms for visitors, living room, kitchen, bathroom and games room.

We try to live with as little impact on the environment as possible. We are off grid and produce our own electricity from solar and wind and compost our toilet waste.

Some organic fruit and vegetables are grown in the garedens and help is always appreciated.

If you are interested in visiting, please contact us via e-mail and we will let you know the date of the next work weekend. We hold around six work weekends throughout the year and all visitors are welcome.

Work weekends are a good opportunity to meet members, have communal meals and get to know how the place work.

We are open to new members and occasionally have vacancies;the first meeting preferably being at a work weekend.

We have a down to earth vibe and DIY culture.

Public transport is available but minimal.

Over 18s
20

Under 18s
7

Year started
1978

Situation
rural

Ideological focus
ecological

Legal structure
industrial and provident society

Open to new members?
yes

Charge visitors?
yes

Work in lieu?
yes

L ilac means Low Impact Living Affordable Community. We are an affordable, urban co-housing development in Leeds, West Yorkshire and have a unique shared ownership model which is the first of its kind in the world. Our community consists of 20 private strawbale and timber eco-homes of different sizes, grouped around our shared common house and pond. Lilac is home to 33 adult members and 12 children, one dog, three cats, chickens and a lot of frogs.

Our site is designed using co-housing principles with shared facilities in the middle such as our common house with its dining room for communal meals, parlour for films, games and meetings, and guest rooms. We also have a shared workshop, launderette, a large play area, and lots of shared green space, allotments and gardens.

Our legal structure is a Mutual Home Ownership Society (MHOS) which is an equity based leaseholder scheme. The cost of the project is divided into equity shares which are allocated to members based on the size of their property and their income. The member buys their allocation of shares either on a monthly basis, in which case their payments are set at 35% of their net income, or in full on moving in. Members can take their equity with them on leaving, and the value of the equity shares is linked to average national earnings, ensuring the project remains affordable from one generation of residents to the next.

We are committed to sharing our learning and model with other groups, and run regular study days and tours. Please see our website for details.

LILAC

Location
Lilac Grove, Victoria Park Avee
Leeds LS5 3AG

Telephone
07890 809143

Electronic Mail
info@lilac.coop

Over 18s
33

Under 18s
12

Year started
2008

Situation
urban

Ideological focus
low impact, affordable, community

Legal structure
industrial and provident society

Open to new members?
yes

Charge visitors?
yes

Work in lieu?
yes

World Wide Web *www.lilac.coop*

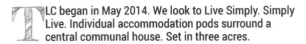

The Loke Community

TLC began in May 2014. We look to Live Simply. Simply Live. Individual accommodation pods surround a central communal house. Set in three acres.

We enjoy dancing, music making, camp cook outs, sailing, paragliding, emotional curiosity, having a laugh and communal cooking. Current members interests include contact improv, chess, yoga, jujitsu, golf biodanza, cycling, movie nights, spoon carving, bowl turning, falconry, sailing, paragliding, story telling, poetry, gardening cookery. Everybody gathers at 8:30am each morning for: check in and share in, group meal 6:30pm

Location
67 Cromer Road
Mundesley
NR11 8DF

Telephone
07880 555235

Electronic Mail
thelokecommunity@gmail.com

Over 18s
5

Year started
2014

Situation
rural

Ideological focus
creating happiness

Legal structure
company limited by guarantee

Open to new members?
yes

Charge visitors?
no

Work in lieu?
no

Lothlorien is a therapeutic community for people with mental health problems. It has been run since 1989 by the Rokpa Trust, an international charity founded by Dr. Akong Tulku Rinpoche of Samye Ling Tibetan Centre in Dumfriesshire. Buddhist values of compassion and tolerance are the basis of our approach, but we are not a religious community and are open to everyone.

Lothlorien Community

The community consists of 10 residents with mental health problems and 4 voluntary co-workers, living in the 13 bedroomed main house and a further 5 people living in the move-on house, Roan Lodge, The 6 staff, known as the Core Group, come in on weekdays. The community has 17 acres of land, including vegetable gardens, woodland and pasture land.

Lothlorien Community is based on the therapeutic community model, which includes principles of collective responsibility and empowerment. Each community member is encouraged to share equally in decision making about community affairs.

At Lothlorien, we have a strong belief in everyone's potential for well being, even in the midst of pain and distress. We believe that people need not be imprisoned by their past. We avoid diagnosing or labelling, and attempt to break down the distinction which frequently exists between those seen as 'well' and those seen as 'unwell'. As a therapeutic community, we aim to help people to develop their strengths and work towards recovery through the shared experience of community life. The ordinary practical tasks of community life, such as gardening, cooking and cleaning, have a grounding effect and the rhythm of daily life provides a structure which helps restore a sense of balance to people's lives. Tara Rokpa Therapy methods such as relaxation, artwork and massage are part of the programme, as well as regular sessions of Qigong.

Location
Corsock
Castle Douglas
DG7 3DR

Telephone
01644 440602

Electronic Mail
contact@lothlorien.tc

Over 18s
21

Year started
1974

Situation
rural

Ideological focus
buddhist

Legal structure
registered charity

Open to new members?
yes

Charge visitors?
yes

Work in lieu?
no

World Wide Web *www.lothlorien.tc*

The Nevill Community

Location
31 Nevill Road
London
N16 8SL

Electronic Mail
thenevillcommunity
@gmail.com

The Nevill is a large converted pub, hosting a small community of various ages and from various places. Our shared values are mutual care, sustainable living, respect, vegetarianism, and participation. We like to welcome nice visitors of all kinds. This house has lots of history and communal spaces, including dining, room, spare rooms, photographic dark room, garden, little library for book exchange, cellar, workshop and bike shed. The household is currently made up of 6 adults, 2 children, 1 cat, and has been founded in 1991 by Dave. We share many interests such as art, architecture, music, film, theatre, activism, DIY, football and the pub quiz! Some of us brew beer, bake bread, enjoy gardening and board games... We usually share meals in the evenings, taking turns to cook for each other, and we all share responsibly house duties without rotas (cleaning, shopping, repairing, etc...).

Over 18s
6

Under 18s
2

Year started
1991

Situation
urban

Ideological focus
political, vegetarian

Legal structure
co-operative society

Open to new members?
yes

Charge visitors?
yes

Work in lieu?
no

Nutclough Tavern has been a housing co-op since 2002, however we are a relatively new group looking to rebuild a co-op with a new identity.

The co-op is situated in the beautiful and historic mill town of Hebden Bridge. The building is Nutclough Tavern, a renovated pub and grade II listed building, with private rooms, and many communal areas such as a large kitchen, dining and living spaces, studio spaces, and a three-tiered garden.

We have recently become a full-house and the current members are aged between 22-46, and we have a lovely dog and cat. We are all interested and invested in the arts and various creative outputs, and like to host and facilitate events, exhibitions, talks, and various other activities in our studio. We intend in the future to make further use of our large garden, and risograph machine, offering both for public use.

Nutclough Housing Co-operative is a member of Radical Routes, a network of co-operatives working for social change.

Nutclough Housing Co-op

Location
Nutclough Tavern
6-8 Nutclough
Hebden Bridge
HX7 8HA

Electronic Mail
nutcloughcoop@gmail.com

Over 18s
7

Year started
2002

Situation
semi-rural

Ideological focus
ecological

Legal structure
industrial and provident society

Open to new members?
yes

Charge visitors?
yes

Work in lieu?
yes

Oakleigh

Location
S4 7AG

Electronic Mail
*susannah.diamond
@gmail.com*

Over 18s
8

Year started
2000

Situation
urban

Ideological focus
none

Legal structure
private ownership

Open to new members?
yes

Charge visitors?
no

Work in lieu?
no

Oakleigh comfortably accommodates 8 people, and the house is so lovely and spacious that occupants tend to stay for 3-10 years before moving on. However sometimes we host volunteers or guests on short courses in Sheffield, and at other times the house is quieter when several people are away. This gives the house an ever changing rhythm with times when only a couple of people are around or larger communal meals with an eclectic combination of dishes and personalities. Interests currently represented in the house include cooking and food growing, crafts and game playing, music and dance, yoga and qi gong, through to foraging and preserving, sustainable living and volunteering.

The house is privately owned, but house meetings three or four times a year offer everyone a say about changes. Housekeeping is managed in a flexible way, with a balance between communally purchased and private sharing of food, and a light-touch approach to recycling, cleaning and maintenance.

The house was initially bought in 2000 with support from the Ecological Building Society. It needed considerable work (plumbing, electrics, improved/secondary windows, and a new back porch), but it is becoming a beautiful home. The restoration of the house was as sympathetic and as low impact as possible, investing in eco-insulation, solar hot water, condensing boiler, efficient wood stove, low emission paints, and solar PV. Other additions have included a pond, woodpile shelter, raised beds for fruit and veg, a chicken house and a friendly dog. We are located in Burngreave, an easy 15 min from Sheffield town centre by bus or bike (30 min walk), and 5 minutes from shops and the Northern General Hospital. The house has a large garden with mature trees and birdsong and offers most amenities, including big screen film nights by the toasty wood-burner.

W e are a small land based community with many transient members from all walks of life who aspire to live simply in tune with land and seasons. Our 100 acres is an upland sheep farm which we manage more as a nature reserve.

We would like to find others who share some of our passions for the arts, agriculture, archaeology and the natural world to live here on a longer term basis.

We do some archaeology, produce most of our own vegetables, meat and milk, cheese and honey, wines, use alternative energy and have restored some beautiful old buildings. We manage our own woodlands for fuel and timber for our natural building projects. We run a programme of courses in prehistoric arts and traditional crafts and are reconstructing a working neolithic settlement. We would like to create a welcoming and inspiring cultural/educational centre that will both provide a fulfilling way of life on the land and look for simple practical solutions to some of the challenges we face today in a rapidly changing world.

Old Chapel Farm

Location
Tylwych
Llanidloes
SY18 6JR

Telephone
01686 413857

Electronic Mail
franblockley@yahoo.co.uk

Over 18s
7

Year started
2000

Situation
rural

Ideological focus
sustainability, biodiversity, creative lifestyle, connecting people to land

Open to new members?
yes

Charge visitors?
yes

Work in lieu?
yes

World Wide Web *www.thewildernesstrust.org/*

Old Hall Community

Location
Rectory Hill
East Bergholt
Colchester
CO7 6TG

Electronic Mail
secretary@oldhall.org.uk

Over 18s
45

Under 18s
9

Year started
1974

Situation
rural

Ideological focus
ecological

Legal structure
friendly society

Open to new members?
yes

Charge visitors?
no

Work in lieu?
yes

We are a large community of people who share an old friary, and 70 acres of Suffolk farmland. We share the workload to be nearly self sufficient in food and energy. Our water is heated by a large wood fired biomass boiler we call the dragon and supplemented by a ground source heat pump. A gas fired boiler is used as a last resort back up. We have an array of 120 solar PV panels to provide our electricity and our water comes from our own borehole with mains water back up. All the members have their own private room or rooms. So a family with one or two children are likely to have four rooms. A single person may have one or two rooms depending on their invested capital. Main meals are eaten together in our big communal kitchen/dining room, using our own meat, vegetables, pulses and fruit. Meals are prepared under our rota job system by whomever signs up to cook. The more vegetarians who decide to cook the more meals will become vegetarian. The more meat eaters sign up the more meat will be consumed. The range of food is varied and excellent. Special dietary needs are catered for whenever possible. To make all this happen we each try to do around 15 hours community work a week, jobs include our domestic rota jobs and the mundane and the skilled – and all are valuable! Community work includes milking, cheese making, construction projects, caring for the farm machinery and our animals, growing food, cooking, cleaning, sewing, maintaining the buildings, the orchards and the grounds – and so much more! Because of this communal commitment, members find that they need only work about three days a week outside the community to bring in enough money to pay the bills. We all help and support each other. In the summer months we enjoy help from friends from all over the world who turn up for two weeks at a time. We can host up to four volunteer friends working alongside the members who provide guidance on whatever outdoor tasks are at hand. We also host and organise our own social events that range from, home cinema, play readings, panto, maypole dancing, games, music events and so on. To help our communal living to work we have "Friday meetings" where we discuss ideas, and make decisions by consensus. Sometimes, of course, we have conflict and disagreement – all part of the rich tapestry here!! The children and young people here have a great life climbing trees, cycling, playing ball-games, baking bread, some like gardening! Children in the main, walk or cycle to local schools. When a member has a friend to stay, the member is expected to make a voluntary contribution towards the additional running costs of the community. Likewise when the community invites a guest to stay, they too are invited to make a voluntary contribution towards the shared costs.

World Wide Web *oldhall.org.uk*

We are a cohousing community in Nether Edge, Sheffield and have been living on site since May 2018. We converted a lovely old house which had been used by the NHS for many years into 11 beautiful and unique flats. We then built another 4 houses to complete the community. Our intention is to create a model for other cohousing groups and to engage with our local area to promote ideas of community and sustainability. Residents of On The Brink (OTB) have their own individual living space and there is communal space for the sharing of cooking, eating, gardening, meeting, relaxing and having fun together. We want to share, generate and support events and celebrations in the local community whilst being aware of larger social, environmental and political issues. We are a multi-generational community that is based on companionship, ecological awareness and mutual respect for each other in all our diversity. Currently we are 20 adults and 6 children.

On the Brink

Location
S11 9BB

Electronic Mail
otbcohousing@gmail.com

Over 18s
20

Under 18s
6

Year started
2014

Situation
urban

Legal structure
company limited by guarantee

Charge visitors?
no

Work in lieu?
no

World Wide Web *onthebrink.community*

Othona
Essex

Location
East End Road
Bradwell-on-Sea
Southminster
CM0 7PN

Telephone
01621 776564

Electronic Mail
bradwell@othona.org

Over 18s
5

Year started
1946

Situation
rural

Ideological focus
*Christian; welcoming all faiths
and none*

Legal structure
registered charity

Open to new members?
yes

Charge visitors?
yes

Work in lieu?
yes

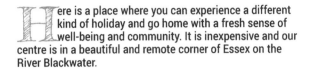

ere is a place where you can experience a different kind of holiday and go home with a fresh sense of well-being and community. It is inexpensive and our centre is in a beautiful and remote corner of Essex on the River Blackwater.

Nearby is the seventh-century Saxon chapel of St Peter-on-the-Wall which we use for twice daily informal worship. We run public events (weekends and weeks) on a variety of themes (e.g. art, music, drama, astronomy, spirituality) for all ages. Our lifestyle is simple and non-dogmatic Christian. We welcome people of all faiths and of none.

Our aim is that through open relationships and shared activities away from the pressures of modern life, we will reach a deeper understanding and acceptance of ourselves and others. We welcome individuals, families, school and church groups. To find out more, please get in touch.

World Wide Web *www.othona-bradwell.org.uk*

Parsonage Farm is a small community situated on the edge of the village of Burwell, twelve miles from Cambridge and five miles from Newmarket. Our community is much more about people, relationships and unity than it is about land, buildings and lifestyle. We are open to new members in principle, but our turnover is very low and we expect to get to know people for a long time first.

Parsonage
Farm

Location
CB25

Electronic Mail
farm@parsonage1.plus.com

Over 18s
5

Year started
1971

Situation
rural

Ideological focus
none

Legal structure
industrial and provident society

Open to new members?
yes

Charge visitors?
no

Work in lieu?
no

Pendragon Community

Location
Pendragon House
Butleigh Road
Glastonbury BA6 8AQ

Telephone
01458 830135

Electronic Mail
roger@pendragoncommunity.com

Over 18s
9

Under 18s
6

Year started
2013

Situation
urban

Ideological focus
sustainability

Legal structure
private ownership

Open to new members?
yes

Charge visitors?
no

Work in lieu?
yes

Pendragon House is located close to the heart of Glastonbury, 5 minutes from both the High Street and the bottom of the Tor, yet right on the edge of the countryside. The house has rooms and suites for residents and guests. We live together communally as family, sharing in one another's lives; living here involves being prepared to work on the things that arise when living closely with others. We aim for low impact living and zero fossil fuel use, although we are not fanatical about it. Long-term community members mainly have outside jobs, pay into the not for profit community fund, and do not work at the community other than the normal house cleaning and everyday chores. We usually eat communally, and all take part in cooking or clearing up when necessary. Such work is currently organised on an 'organic' co-operative basis rather than with a formal schedule. The commune has a cat. Children may be home educated or may go to the local schools. We have a large meeting room and art studio that are used for everyday commune activity and events and workshops. The organic garden and orchard is maintained by volunteers, we often have wwoofers who look after light maintenance that arises through everyday activity and gardening; sometimes help out with children etc. We are omnivorous but there is a vegetarian fridge and vegetarians or vegans are catered for. We often cook huge organic apple pies with apples from our orchard, which we freeze and use year-round. We are 5 minutes' walk from Glastonbury town centre, 10 minutes' to the schools and ten minutes' to the base of Glastonbury Tor. The town is an eclectic place with a lively music scene, alternative culture and tourism. We occasionally have concerts in our event room and our midday Sunday 'Dance Church' (not religious) with visiting DJs has been going every week for more than 4 years. The house has 3 family size suites and several other rooms for individuals. There are wood burning stoves, a biomass boiler, a wood burning Aga, plus electric hob and oven in the kitchen and other electric necessities powered by a combination of Solar and grid. Big south facing windows let the sun do a lot of warming in winter. We have no gas connection or oil burner, and electricity is not used for heating. We are currently looking for individuals and also a family with ideally young to early teens children, but the most important thing is to be motivated for communal living. A long term goal is to transfer ownership of the house to a Trust.

World Wide Web *www.pendragonhouse.org*

Pilsdon Community offers a refuge for anyone who needs a safe place to stay at a particular point in their life, some come whilst recovering from alcoholism or addiction, others coping with mental illness or following a crisis point in their life. Run by residential community members we offer friendship, hospitality, acceptance and many cups of tea.

Pilsdon Community

The Pilsdon Community is a smallholding of 12 acres with cows, sheep, pigs, chickens and ducks and a large vegetable garden. We rear our own meat, grow our own vegetables and make our own dairy produce. Everyone is invited to participate fully in the life of the community from milking a cow to digging up a parsnip or preparing afternoon tea and toast.

Community members plus their families and seasonal volunteers live in and have responsibility for the Community (not salaried but supported). We share broadly in a Christian spirituality, participate in daily prayer/meditation and enjoy the privilege of offering hospitality. We are often remembered for our good food! We are by necessity strictly alcohol-free.

Pilsdon offer periods of respite for people who may need space for recuperation in a supportive and caring environment, welcoming those from all backgrounds and from many different walks of life – whether young or old, rich or poor. Pilsdon is a community that shares a common life of prayer, hospitality and work, providing an environment of acceptance and friendship where people can begin to rebuild their lives.

Location
Pilsdon Manor
Pilsdon
Bridport
DT6 5NZ

Telephone
01308 868308

Electronic Mail
pilsdon@pilsdon.org.uk

Year started
1958

Situation
rural

Ideological focus
christian

Legal structure
registered charity

Open to new members?
yes

Charge visitors?
yes

Work in lieu?
yes

World Wide Web *www.pilsdon.org.uk*

Postlip Community

Postlip Hall is a beautiful, large, Grade 1 listed Jacobean manor house with 15 acres of land, nestling in a quiet valley, surrounded by woods, just below the highest point in the Cotswolds. It's divided into eight family living units. Members' ages range from 0yrs to 78yrs. Most adults work outside Postlip and, although we all eat together fairly frequently, we live independent family lives. Postlip works as a Housing Association, meeting formally every month to discuss, plan, inform and make decisions.

Each family or individual holds a long lease from the Association and can sell it back at an agreed valuation if they want to leave. The Association then recruits a new family to buy in by advertising in "Members Needed" on this site and elsewhere.

Our legal structure means that you can only live here if you're a member and a leaseholder. We're sad that this stops us offering living space to other people, but we haven't been able to find a way around it. And we're also sad that it's hard to find room for long-term visitors or volunteers. We're set up to look after visitors on our monthly WWOOF weekends though, and very much enjoy having visitors then – we've been a WWOOF farm from the start.

We all pay a monthly ground rent, supplemented by income from the many events we organise, both in our magnificent 14th century tithe barn, from the annual Cotswold Beer Festival, to barn dances, folk music weekends and wedding celebrations to more intimate musical and dramatic performances in the main hall.

We work communally in our organic vegetable garden, look after our sheep and chickens and maintain and improve the woods, grounds and walls of the estate.

Children are an important part of being here and thrive in the space and the opportunities that life at Postlip offers them. We all try to live lightly on the earth and aim to leave Postlip a better place for those who follow. If you'd like to get to know Postlip better then the best way is to work alongside us on our monthly WWOOF weekends. Email us to find out more.

Location
Postlip Hall
Winchcombe
Cheltenham
GL54 5AQ

Telephone
07866378413

Electronic Mail
postlip.applicants@gmail.com

Over 18s
15

Under 18s
12

Year started
1970

Situation
rural

Ideological focus
none

Open to new members?
yes

Charge visitors?
no

Work in lieu?
yes

World Wide Web *www.postliphall.org.uk*

We're a small housing co-operative of 5 adults living in a shared house in south east London, which we bought in 2020. We'd describe ourselves as left-leaning, and most of us are involved in political or community activism. We aim to balance a certain degree of communal living (e.g. sharing communal space and some meals) with the freedom for each of us to live our own independent lives.

We are using a form of housing co-op known as a mutual home ownership society, which means that some of our rent goes towards building up an equity stake in the house (as if we were each paying off our own mortgage). This means that when one of us leaves, they would be entitled to take this money with them. This type of co-op isn't currently common in the UK, but we feel that this is a better model in London at the moment because it helps to compensate for the fact that our rent is unfortunatley not cheap, and because it will hopefully put people in a better position to secure decent housing if they have to move on in future.

When we're not looking for new members we are very happy to provide advice and assistance to anyone thinking about starting their own small housing co-op – please feel free to contact us if you are interested in this.

Quaggy Housing Co-op

Location
SE14 6HW

Electronic Mail
*quaggymhoslondon
@gmail.com*

Over 18s
5

Year started
2020

Situation
urban

Legal structure
co-operative society

Charge visitors?
no

Work in lieu?
no

World Wide Web *https://quaggycoop.wordpress.com*

Quaker Community

Location
Water Lane
Bamford
Hope Valley S33 0DA

Telephone
01433 650085

Electronic Mail
mail
@quakercommunity.org.uk

Over 18s
8

Year started
1988

Situation
semi-rural

Ideological focus
quaker

Legal structure
charitable incorporated organisation

Open to new members?
yes

Charge visitors?
yes

Work in lieu?
no

Ｗe are a community of 5 to 10 Quakers with a focus on leading a spirit-led life in an ecologically sustainable way. We welcome guests from all faiths and none. We run a range of led courses, events and retreats; these range from the reflective and spiritual to hands-on work in the 10 acres of reclaimed woodland, wetland, wild-flower meadow and organic fruit and vegetable gardens which we have managed since the Community was started in 1988.

We also welcome individuals on self-catering retreats, and self-catered groups of up to 16 (if sharing – more if also camping). We are in beautiful semi-rural surroundings in the Peak District, with a wide range of hill and riverside walks from the doorstep and bus and train links to Sheffield and Manchester. Short and long term volunteering placements are available on an individually negotiated basis, please contact us for more information.

We review our on-going membership on a three-yearly basis and are open to membership enquiries from Quakers and attenders.

World Wide Web *www.quakercommunity.org.uk*

ainbow, known by many as 'The Street', has twenty-four terraced houses in one street situated in the north of Milton Keynes. The Co operative was founded in 1977. The aim of the group is to provide housing in a community setting, there is a communal garden with a natural pond, fruit trees and play areas for the children.

The membership, generally 35 to 40 including children is very mixed in age, sex and personal circumstances. One house is used as a Community House and has meeting space, office, laundry facilities, a workshop equipped with tools, freezer, domestic equipment and greenhouse.

Provision has been made for disabled people with wheelchair access by means of a portable ramp. Some members are vegetarian or vegan, although this is not a pre-requisite for membership.

Membership is by application and prospective members are expected to participate in the activities of the co-op, including work days and meetings, before being eligible for membership and therefore housing. It often takes some time before prospective members are successful, as the turnover of houses is infrequent and there are many people waiting.

The co-op is run by general meeting (all members participate in decision making) and most of the maintenance of the property and management of the co-op is done by members.

Rainbow Housing Co-operative

Location
9 Spencer Street
New Bradwell
Milton Keynes
MK13 0DW

Electronic Mail
rainbowhousingcoop
@gmail.com

Over 18s
31

Under 18s
6

Year started
1977

Situation
urban

Legal structure
industrial and provident society

Open to new members?
yes

Charge visitors?
no

Work in lieu?
no

Redfield

Redfield is an intentional community situated in North Buckinghamshire. We live as a single household in a large old mansion, set in 17 acres of gardens, woodland and pasture, surrounded by farmland. We have sheep, pigs, chickens and bees.

Life here involves a lot of sharing, commitment, responsibility, building maintenance, gardening, animal management, logging and having fun. The ground floor of the house and the grounds are communal, with private rooms and units on the first and second floors.

Location
*Buckingham Rd, Winslow
Buckingham MK18 3LZ*

Telephone
01296 713661

Electronic Mail
info@redfieldcommunity.org.uk

The Redfield Centre is a separate self contained venue with accommodation spaces and a classroom space with a workshop attached which could be hired for similar minded groups/ individuals. Please visit the Redfield Centre website for more info www.redfieldcentre.wordpress.com

We all have part-time jobs and pay a monthly rent to the co-op; we commit a minimum of 16 hours per week to the community. In recent years, members' outside jobs have included accountancy, forestry, lecturing, planning, nursing, teaching, lorry driving, and care work. Members also run their own businesses from the Community, these currently include a mobile refill shop, Tatooing, Teaching music, Wood milling, Photography and Yoga classes.

Over 18s
10

Under 18s
6

Year started
1978

Redfield is a registered Housing Co-operative and we make all our decisions by consensus at our fortnightly meeting. We welcome visitors on our visitor days, as WWOOFers or as volunteers during our 2 maintenance weeks.

Situation
rural

Ideological focus
community life & sustainability

Legal structure
industrial and provident society

Open to new members?
yes

Charge visitors?
yes

Work in lieu?
yes

World Wide Web *www.redfieldcommunity.org.uk*

O ur future is bright. Maybe you want to be a part of it? Like any good diverse permaculture garden, our community needs a variety of people in order to flourish and grow further.

We welcome applicants and open the doors for the next generation of Rubha Phoil members: If you come and stay with us for a while, you'll have the chance to experience living in community and with nature on a daily basis. Learn to redesign your life, live sustainably, reconnect with nature, build community. It will be a rich learning experience for all of us.

We love things how they are at Rubha Phoil. But to take us to the next level and make our home even more special, there are some important jobs to be done. We often need people who are willing to lead on projects. We can offer workshops, the 4 month Community Building Program and a potential membership of the community. Food and accommodation can be provided and we can also discuss monetary reimbursement.

At the time of writing our projects include building a new shower bock and finishing an existing one; and widening and resurfacing our track. You don't need to have the hands-on skills for this work, just the momentum and desire to organise and lead the project. There'll be plenty of help from our team.

Rubha Phoil

Location
IV45 8RS

Electronic Mail
info@earth-ways.co.uk

Over 18s
5

Year started
2016

Situation
rural

Ideological focus
permaculture, nature based community

Open to new members?
yes

Charge visitors?
yes

Work in lieu?
yes

World Wide Web *www.rubhaphoil.org*

Sanford Housing Co-op

Location
11 Sanford Walk
London
SE14 6NB

Telephone
020 8692 7316

Electronic Mail
mark.langford@cds.coop

We have beautiful ponds, gardens and a friendly atmosphere, a tropical communal oasis in London with a famous colourful peace movement mural. Many performers and artists live here and we have tried to artistically redesign our living space.

Founded in 1973 it was built using private finance supplied by the Housing Corporation and Commercial Union. Sanford Housing Co-op consists of 119 units of shared accommodation in 14 purpose-built houses. Its rents are not set by any outside body but are designed to cover actual costs. All the tenants as members of the Co-operative are collectively landlords and responsible for helping the Co-op to protect their interests and to save the Co-op money by their voluntary work.

Sanford actively seeks applicants from all sections of the community, over the age of 18, who wish to live in a Co-operative, regardless of gender, ethnic origin, disability, sexual orientation or health status. Sanford is a single person co-operative and is not suitable for applicants who have dependent children or who wish to live as a couple.

Over 18s
119

Year started
1973

Situation
urban

Ideological focus
none

Legal structure
community benefit society

Open to new members?
yes

Charge visitors?
no

Work in lieu?
no

World Wide Web *www.sanford.coop/*

Founded in 2015, Scraptoft Housing Co-op is a large house with a lovely garden, also sharing an additional extended garden with two of our neighbours. Our collective gardens hold open grass, flowers, trees, vegetable plots, an orchard, chicken co-ops, a cabin, and it backs out onto the local allotments.

As a community, we care about social change. Many of our members are involved in activism in different ways, and we try our best to support and accommodate each others varying needs.

We care about our impact on the world, and are steadily trying to make this a sustainable living space, and would welcome anyone bringing new ideas and energy to that goal.

Members of our community enjoy board games, crafts, outside activities, cooking, gardening, etc.

We are open for visitors, and prospective new members. So if you care about sustainability, community, and making the world a better place, please get in touch

Scraptoft Housing Co-op

Location
105 Scraptoft Lane
Leicester
LE5 2FE

Electronic Mail
pam@phonecoop.coop

Over 18s
5

Year started
2015

Situation
suburban

Legal structure
industrial and provident society

Open to new members?
yes

Charge visitors?
no

Work in lieu?
no

Share Instead

We are a relatively new housing co-op in Sheffield, since 2015. In our house, costs and responsibilities are shared and we run on co-operative principles. We are a mainly vegetarian and vegan-friendly household who share cooking and costs of food, and grow some food together. We are striving to live sustainably and support our members to work for peace and social change. We are a member of the Radical Routes network. If you are interested in knowing more about us get in touch.

Location
S7 1DS

Electronic Mail
shareinstead@gmail.com

Over 18s
5

Year started
2012

Situation
urban

Ideological focus
working for peace and social change

Legal structure
industrial and provident society

Open to new members?
yes

Charge visitors?
yes

Work in lieu?
no

World Wide Web *www.sheffield.coop/wiki/share_Instead*

S hirle Hill Cohousing is a thriving, developing and learning community of ten households in Nether Edge, Sheffield, aged from 2 to 74. We took over the acre of grounds and an old stately home turned NHS childrens centre and have revived it with five flats in the victorian/georgian house and five new Ecohouses in the grounds.

We aim to share tasks, work, meals and fun as much as possible, while maintaining our own independence and privacy with our own front doors. We are lucky to share a large living room, dining room/kitchen, laundry, developing garden and allotment and bike and car storage. We aim to be as environmentally friendly as possible within our means and play an active part in our local community.

Shirle Hill
Cohousing

Location
6 Shirle Hill
Sheffield
S11 9DY

Electronic Mail
helloshirlehill@gmail.com

Over 18s
17

Under 18s
3

Year started
2013

Situation
urban

Ideological focus
values based, environmental features, supportive community

Legal structure
company limited by guarantee

Charge visitors?
no

Work in lieu?
no

Skylark Housing Co-op

Location
BN2

Electronic Mail
info@skylarkhousingcoop.org.uk

Skylark Housing Co-operative consits of seven adults and three dogs. On the 1st March 2013 we bought our semi-detached house. It's an ex-council house on the edge of the downs, in Bevendean. In our large garden our fig tree produces wonderfully and we grow vegetetables, flowers and herbs.

Bevendean has a vibrant community scene with the first co-operative pub on a council estate The Bevy, a plethora of other housing co-operatives, a community garden and a fruit and nut orchard in the works.

All of us at Skylark are queer and many trans/non-binary. We are involved in activism, education and community activities. Its not all graft though and members can also be found knitting, massaging, drawing and painting, making music, gardening, and studying. If you would like to apply for membership have a look at our website.

Over 18s
7

Year started
2009

Situation
urban

Legal structure
industrial and provident society

Open to new members?
yes

Charge visitors?
no

Work in lieu?
no

World Wide Web *www.skylarkhousingcoop.org.uk*

Springhill Cohousing is the first new build Cohousing Community in the UK and the first project of the Cohousing Company. The search for land started in 1999 and the site in Stroud was acquired in 2000. Very soon after, all the plots were pre-sold to members who designed the community and layout of their own houses/flats.

The principles of Cohousing are consensus decision making, pedestrianised estate, large common house for shared evening meals, private self-contained units.

The 35 houses, flats and studios are super-insulated, 20 houses have 49 kWp of PV solar panels, there is a car share scheme and the site is Town Centre. There are a number of committees eg. Kitchen, Garden, Parking, Disputes etc. which are mandated to make decisions. The idea is to reduce the number of large meetings and trust small groups to make decisions.

Joining is by self selection. The only criteria are that the new members agree with the principles of Cohousing and can afford to buy in. There are often rooms available for lodgers and houses and flats become available to rent or buy from time to time. Please register interest via the web site.

Springhill Cohousing Community

Location
Springfield Road
Stroud
GL5 1TN

Electronic Mail
info@springhillcohousing.com

Over 18s
50

Under 18s
32

Year started
2000

Situation
urban

Ideological focus
cohousing/consensus

Legal structure
company limited by shares

Open to new members?
yes

Charge visitors?
yes

Work in lieu?
no

Talamh

Location
Birkhill House
Coalburn
ML11 0NJ

Electronic Mail
talamh@riseup.net

Over 18s
6

Under 18s
2

Year started
1993

Situation
rural

Ideological focus
diy/environmental

Legal structure
industrial and provident society

Open to new members?
yes

Charge visitors?
no

Work in lieu?
yes

Talamh is gaelic for earth, and it's 50 acres form a green haven in Lanarkshire just south of Glasgow. The thousands of young native trees planted over the past two decades are growing into woodland, and the pond we created teems with life – the historic land and buildings here provides a mixed habitat for wildlife and people. The current members and an extensive wider community of all ages call this amazing place home. Talamh Housing co-op is Landlord free and organised by the current members. At weekly meetings (as a group) we manage the affairs and aim to achieve decision making by consensus. Day to day living functions in an informal, unstructured way, and there are always various projects ongoing that everyone can get involved in. Successfully self-organising in this way relies on co-operation and communication. The motivation comes from sustainable and low-impact living by creating, building, making, mending, growing, tattie digging, chip eating, healing, cooking, waste reducing , brainstorming, finding solutions, supporting one another, restoration, cycling, recycling, upcycling, reusing, repurposing, relaxing, discussing, making do, music, dreaming, dancing, problem solving, caring, art, gardening, laughing, learning, sharing, feasting, merrymaking, baking, brewing, celebrating and other stuff. We host indoor & outdoor events, workshops, discussion groups, skillshares & gatherings. There is lots of space for camping and visitors. Volunteers are welcome to visit by arrangement, to get involved with the various projects here and experience community life and day to day goings on.

World Wide Web *www.facebook.com/talamh.house*

Taliesin Housing Co-operative purchased Temperance House in Machynlleth, Wales, with a loan from Triodos Bank. It is a lovely house, in a beautiful location which would benefit from more enthusiastic community minded folk to help move the Co-op forward a bit. We are based in the Dyfi valley, West Wales, an area full of woodlands,nature reserves and beautiful beaches. We are close to the sea (you can see it from the house!) and a bus ride away from Machynlleth (quirky/alternative market town) and Aberystwyth (lively seaside town with independant shops and thriving music scene). There is an alternative, political scene in the area which is well integrated with the local Welsh community and great outdoors.There are many local groups and social activities to get involved in.We share the cost of all bills and running of the house and also have shared basic foods, we eat together when we can but this is not always practical due to people's different schedules.

Taliesin Housing Co-operative

Location
Temperance House
Machynlleth
SY20 8JH

Electronic Mail
julestomo@yahoo.com

Over 18s
3

Situation
rural

Legal structure
industrial and provident society

Open to new members?
yes

Charge visitors?
no

Work in lieu?
no

Taraloka Buddhist Retreat Centre for Women

Location
Taraloka Retreat Centre
Bettisfield
Whitchurch
SY13 2LD

Telephone
01948 710646

Electronic Mail
admin@taraloka.org.uk

Taraloka is both a community and a Buddhist retreat centre for women, to which women come from all over the world to practise meditation and go deeper into the teachings of the Buddha. The centre has been running since 1985 and offers a beautiful environment in which to practise stillness and simplicity.

All of us living here are committed to Buddhist ideals and to creating the best possible facilities for women to come on retreat. For the purposes of our work, people have individual responsibilities for different work areas, for example cooking, maintenance or leading retreats. We all actively pursue the Buddhist way of life, following a daily programme of meditation, work and communal meals. We live simply and communally with a strong emphasis on ethical practice, aiming for more kindness, generosity, contentment, truthful speech and clarity of mind. Apart from our respective team meetings, we hold weekly community meetings and business meetings. We aim to be friendly and co-operative and decisions are arrived at through consensus. Taraloka is registered as a charity and all members receive the same basic support. We are all part of the Buddhist Movement the Triratna Buddhist Community and we don't have a system for accommodating volunteers from outside of the movement to work here. We have a range of retreats, some for those who are completely new to meditation and Buddhism, and some for those who currently practice within our tradition. We also have an Open Day every two years.

For further information about our retreats please contact the office or see our website.

Over 18s
12

Year started
1985

Situation
rural

Ideological focus
buddhist

Charge visitors?
yes

Work in lieu?
no

World Wide Web *www.taraloka.org.uk*

Temple Druid community is set in 56 acres in the foothills of the Preseli Mountains. Our aim is to be a year-round Therapeutic and Educational Centre within a sustainable farm, woodland environment, orchard and kitchen garden. The majority of our projects have a particular focus of working with vulnerable children, young people, and their families. We work with the Permaculture ethics of earth care, people care, and a fair share for everyone.

We are dreaming into the future and making tentative plans for the renovation and extension so the grade II listed house; planting trees and creating forest gardens; improving growing areas/composting and always from the perspective of being guardians of this land, and wanting to keep the beauty alive and eventually pass on the ever-healthier land to the next generation. We only have rooms in the main house for individuales, couples or families to rent at the moment.

We are also open for new director/members, this does require a financial investment into Temple Druid Ltd. But we do want prospective director/members to rent for at least 18 months before considering investing any money into the not for profit Temple Druid Ltd company. Whilst it is not necessary to have experience in a particular area of land stewardship, working with vulnerable people, community living, business management, teaching and renovations, the current community would greatly benefit from people with those skills or a can-do attitude!

For further information see our website and give us a call.

Temple Druid Community

Location
SA66 7XS

Electronic Mail
james@templedruid.org

Over 18s
7

Under 18s
3

Year started
2014

Situation
rural

Ideological focus
be

Legal structure
company limited by guarantee

Open to new members?
yes

Charge visitors?
yes

Work in lieu?
yes

World Wide Web *www.templedruid.org*

Threshold Centre

The Threshold Centre at Cole Street Farm, is a small cohousing community just outside Gillingham in North Dorset. We aim to 'walk our talk' with a lifestyle that is more green, more affordable, and more neighbourly.

The Threshold Centre consists of fourteen dwellings, seven of which are affordable rent and shared ownership with a local housing association – a first in the short history of cohousing in this country. There is also a common farmhouse with shared facilities and guest rooms, green energy systems and a community vegetable garden.

Location
Cole Street Farm
Cole Street Lane
Gillingham
SP8 5JQ

Telephone
01747 821929

Electronic Mail
info@thresholdcentre.org.uk

We hold an open afternoon tea on the first Saturday of the month and Gardening Weekends and other events periodically. Please see our website for details of dates. If you are interested in coming to live here, you are welcome to visit, even if there are no immediate vacancies.

Please see our website or email us for more details.

Over 18s
18

Year started
2004

Situation
rural

Legal structure
community interest company

Open to new members?
yes

Charge visitors?
yes

Work in lieu?
yes

World Wide Web *www.thresholdcentre.org.uk*

Tinkers Bubble is a small woodland community which uses environmentally sound methods of working the land without fossil fuels. We have planning permission for self-built houses on the condition that we make a living from the land. We make our monetary incomes mainly through forestry, apple work and gardening. As a result we're money poor but otherwise rich! We manage about 28 acres of douglas fir, larch, and mixed broadleaf woodland using horses, two person saws, and a wood-fired steam-powered sawmill. Our pastures, orchards, and gardens are organically certified, and no-dig methods are commonly used. We press apple juice for sale, grow most of our own vegetables, keep chickens and bees, and sell our produce at farmers markets. We make loads of jam, cheese, butter, preserves, cider and wine. We have solar powered 12v electricity, spring water on tap, and use compost toilets. We burn wood for cooking, heating, and for hot water in the bathhouse. We eat some meat (mostly game), and try to cater for all diets. Though some of us would consider ourselves to be spiritual, we have no shared spirituality. Most people wash their clothes by hand. Life is lived mostly outdoors, so it's cold in the winter, but we live on the top of a steep hill, so there's plenty of chances to get warm! There's loads of wildlife on site, particularly badgers, deer and ticks!We're currently a group of 10 adults, spanning a wide age range, and 2 young children. We are sometimes open to new live-in members who are interested in making a living from the land, although there is an expectation that you volunteer with us for a while as we get to know each other, before we commit to new membership. Please get in touch by email or post if you would like to volunteer with us, including why you're interested in visiting, and any relevant experience you've got. We don't expect you to be a professional peasant; It just helps to get an idea of what you're about. Please check your spam folder for our response – we try to answer all emails, usually within a week or so, but some email providers (particularly hotmail) seem to put all emails from riseup.net in the spam folder (please let us know if this is the case). We have a guest house with a wood burner, but long-johns are still a must in winter. Bring a torch, warm clothes, practical footwear, and any fresh looking roadkill you find en-route. Follow the Tinkers bubble blog: tinkersbubble.wordpress.com

Tinker's Bubble

Location
Norton Covert
Little Norton
Norton sub Hamdon
Stoke-sub-Hamdon
TA14 6TE

Electronic Mail
tinkersbubble@riseup.net

Over 18s
10

Under 18s
3

Year started
1994

Situation
rural

Ideological focus
environmental

Open to new members?
yes

Charge visitors?
no

Work in lieu?
yes

World Wide Web *www.tinkersbubble.org*

Tipi Valley

Location
SA32 7UQ

Telephone
07866370936

Electronic Mail
TipiValleyWales@gmail.com

Tipi Valley is situated high in the hills of South-West Wales. Our community has been buying it field by field since 1975. In this time our oldest fields have regenerated from sheep farming land to mixed deciduous woodland rich in wildlife. It's a wild valley dotted with our homes that are low impact dwellings – tipis, yurts and turf roofed round huts.

Living this close to nature and the elements creates a deep connection with the land. We express this in our lives through creative work on our shelters and gardens and get-togethers in our communal tipi, known as the big lodge, where we gather for music and song.

Over the years we have had over 130 home births and our children are either home educated or go to the local bilingual schools.

The big lodge tipi is also where visitors stay. We expect our visitors to look after the big lodge by keeping it a tidy and welcoming space. There are also opportunities to help around the valley – if you would like to be involved please enquire on arrival.

Please email us if you would like to visit. For the duration of the pandemic visiting is not possible because there is not the space for social distancing in our Big Lodge.

Over 18s
50

Under 18s
30

Year started
1975

Situation
rural

Ideological focus
low impact

Open to new members?
yes

Charge visitors?
no

Work in lieu?
no

We're a housing co-operative that's been around for over ten years, a mile or so away from the city centre in what is one of the most culturally diverse cities in Britain. We arose from the radical student population of the early 1990s via New Education Housing Co-op and are members of Radical Routes and take part in an awful lot of different things.

We've got two big, beautiful houses 100 yards away from each other, one a five-bedroom Georgian style and the other an eight-bedroomed Grade II listed mansion with office space and a big community room, both of which we rent out to other organisations or else use ourselves for parties, meetings etc. We are a lively group of people that like living collectively and are very diverse in both ages, views and diet, but very definitely are alternative. Our kitchens are collectively vegetarian and communal meals are optional and arise spontaneously, along with our parties.

We are always looking for new members to help us run everything and to replace the ones that have moved on; if you would like to find out more, drop us a line. We are also open to visitors and friends popping in, but ring us first.

Torch Housing Co-op

Location
10 Richmond Road
Hockley
Birmingham
B18 5NH

Telephone
0121 551 3161

Electronic Mail
jantorch@aol.com

Over 18s
9

Year started
1994

Situation
urban

Ideological focus
humanist/pagan

Legal structure
industrial and provident society

Open to new members?
yes

Charge visitors?
no

Work in lieu?
yes

Trelay

Trelay Cohousing is a vibrant community of 23 adults of all ages and nine children. It was established in 2007 on a farm with thirty-two acres in North Cornwall, UK. It is a great place to grow, learn and be, to live sustainably and connect in a healthy way with our planet and each other. A rural retrofit cohousing scheme, we welcome visitors and volunteers interested in our way of living. We work hard, and we have fun.

The main features of our community are:
– it is set up and run by its members co-operatively
– members are consciously committed to living as and contributing to a community
– members all have a private living space as well as the use of communal buildings and land

Examples of our sustainability efforts are:
Environmental
– several solar PV systems
– two Lithium-Ion Tesla PowerWall batteries.
– a ground source heat pump
– an air source heat pump
– an independent sewage system
– shared amenities (e.g. laundry), tools & machines (lawnmower)
– producing our own meat, milk, eggs (and manure for compost)
– growing our vegetables and fruit without chemicals
Social
– a close-knit group that cares and shares
– commitment to continued learning around compassionate/ mindful communication, permaculture
– communal kitchen/dining room for regular shared meals & meetings
– communal indoor area for events, music, dancing, playing, films
– communal garden for BBQs, pizza oven, children's play area, bonfires, hanging out
– interactions with the wider local community: involvement in the Parish Council, choirs, sports clubs, events
Financial
– a communal mortgage facility which enables families/ individuals with little capital to join
– operating a Mutual Home Ownership scheme which enables all members to gain equity in their living space
– sound budgeting and financial management processes.

Location
Trelay Farm
St Gennys
Bude
EX23 0NJ

Telephone
07960707607

Electronic Mail
interest@trelay.org

Over 18s
22

Under 18s
11

Year started
2007

Situation
coastal rural

Ideological focus
sustainability

Legal structure
company limited by guarantee

Open to new members?
yes

Charge visitors?
yes

Work in lieu?
no

World Wide Web *www.trelay.org*

We are a small, friendly, open minded community who have come together to live co-operatively and creatively. Co-operating challenges us to take account of others' needs and place our own needs in that context. This is at the heart of what we're about and the means by which we help each other to grow. We all value living ethically, with compassion and a spirit of generosity.

We have a beautiful converted water mill and outbuildings, with 5 acres of land with woodland and a stream, in our own secluded valley. There is easy access to Llangollen – a vibrant, welcoming town in N E Wales which has good schools.

We live in our own separate households but co-own and co-manage the co-op and share many resources.

Ty Brethyn

Location
Fron Bache
Ty Brethyn
Llangollen
LL20 7BS

Telephone
01978 862944

Electronic Mail
aderynbran@hotmail.com

Over 18s
9

Under 18s
4

Year started
2007

Situation
rural

Legal structure
industrial and provident society

Open to new members?
yes

Charge visitors?
no

Work in lieu?
no

Wellhouse Community

We are small community of 4 to 8 people living in a large, recently purchased 6 bedroom town house with outbuildings, summer house, a workshop, garden and private courtyard. The house is 3 storey and dates back to 1865 having been former residence of the Duke of St Albans. It was purchased for a relatively low price as it needs quite a bit of work although is very habitable. We have an allotment, have a well and have invested in solar panels. The property is deceptively large.

Location
LN7 6TX

Electronic Mail
gytribe1@gmail.com

We are all vegan/vegetarian and so don't have/cook any meat in the kitchen. We usually eat together and support each other taking it in turns to cook, fitting round work schedules. We buy most food and supplies communally (as much possible organic) and try only using eco products. We are trying to reduce our plastic use. All the core adults work. We share bills etc equally and any prospective persons joining us would be expected to share a portion of the house costs. There is rural broadband. We do live to a certain standard of cleanliness and we expect community members to help with aspects of helping maintain the house and garden.

The house is situated in the historic town of Caistor that has roman origins and is on the rolling Lincolnshire hills. There is a Co-op store, pub and several amenities. It's a quiet Lincolnshire town but there is a good sense of community and a surprising number of events.

Over 18s
4
Under 18s
1
Year started
2020
Situation
urban
Ideological focus
vegetarian/vegan eco self sufficiency, community and shared living
Legal structure
private ownership
Open to new members?
yes
Charge visitors?
yes
Work in lieu?
yes

Decisions are taken as collectively as possible and the current house deed holders have been living communally for over 25 years. We are very open to new input and always have been able to resolve any issues in a friendly way. It certainly isn't the usual landlord/tenant relationship, we prefer people to speak openly and say what they think. We are open to short term visitors as well as those wishing to investigate longer term arrangements. We enjoy skill sharing. We are very friendly and run laughter yoga sessions; enjoy music and playing games, walking, animals, meditation, sitting round, drinking tea and chatting. The house is an amazing family home and has huge potential. It is large enough for everyone to find space and we have one room as a dedicated playroom so is a great place to grow up in.

If you think this sounds like something you could get involved with please send an e-mail and let's arrange for a chat, perhaps for you to visit, maybe even join us for a meal?

Wild Peak is a rural housing co-op with land in the Derwent Valley in Derbyshire. Wild Peak Housing Co-op was set up to house people working or volunteering for environmental change and currently our members do both environmental and social change work. We all believe working and living co-operatively is a positive and resilient choice.

We manage our land for conservation along with a some food growing, firewood and hosting events in the summer. We have a feeling of rural isolation whist being only a couple of miles from the town of Belper and a short trip into Derby. As we are next to a local wetland bird reserve we get to share our land with a host of birds and other busy wildlife.

After buying the property in 2012 the co-op has renovated the derelict farm house and out buildings to provide housing for up to 10 adults and dependents. It was a lot of work and we are still aiming to improve with ongoing insulation work and other maintenance tasks. If you would like to know more send us an email, we currently have space for more people and want to build connections with like minded folk. We are a member of Radical Routes.

Wild Peak Housing Co-op

Location
Lawn Cottage
Wyver Lane
Belper
DE56 2EF

Electronic Mail
friendsofwildpeak@gmail.com

Over 18s
6

Under 18s
3

Year started
2012

Situation
rural

Legal structure
co-operative society

Open to new members?
yes

Charge visitors?
no

Work in lieu?
no

World Wide Web *www.facebook.com/wildpeakhousingcoop/about*

Woodhead Community

Location
Kinloss
Forres
IV36 2UE

Telephone
01309 676184

Electronic Mail
info@woodheadcom.org

After over two decades as a small family and land-based community, we officially dismantled some of our communal activities a few years ago. However, the four founders still carry on in much the same way as before, sharing spiritual, political and social values. We continue to work together one day a week, maintaining the property and socialising.

There are two caravans on the site, a garden room, and a room in one of our houses where single people live, sharing a large communal kitchen and living space. They each live independently, having community interactions as they choose. There is also a three bedroomed semi-independant unit (half of the original farm house). Each person living at Woodhead needs to be self financing.

We continue to maintain the property of around 2 acres, providing an abundance of vegetables, fruit, flowers and trees. We have WWOOFers come to work with us, sharing their lives and varied cultures. The founding couples continue to eat together twice a week and maintain the car pool which runs very successfully.

The Findhorn Foundation and its associated wider community is just down the road from us. Its vibrant, international population provides a rich source of inspiration, friendship and culture for us to engage with.

Over 18s
8

Year started
1994

Situation
rural

Ideological focus
collectively living with spirit

Legal structure
none

Open to new members?
yes

Charge visitors?
yes

Work in lieu?
yes

OTHER EXISTING COMMUNITIES

It is always difficult to represent the fluid and ever changing landscape of the different intentional communities in Britain. This section includes communities that we believe are still going but are probably too busy doing interesting things to have updated their listing in the online directory in time for this publication.

Argyle Street Housing Co-op
CB1 3LU
www.ash.coop

Ashram Community
S4 7SN
www.ashram.org.uk

Auchinleck Housing Co-op
EH6 4SG

Balnakeil Craft Village
IV27 4PT
balnakeilcraftvillage.weebly.com

Beech Grove Community
CT15 4HH
www.bruderhof.com

Bhaktivedanta Manor
WD25 8EZ
www.krishnatemple.com

Blackcurrent
JN1 4JQ

Botton Village
YO21 2NJ
www.camphillvillagetrust.org.uk/locations/botton-village

The Burrow Housing Co-op
M11 1JX
www.theburrowcoop.com

Camphill Rudolf Steiner Schools
AB15 9EP
www.camphillschools.org.uk

Carol Street Housing Co-op
NW1 0SE

Catholic Worker Farm
WD3 9J
www.thecatholicworkerfarm.org

Coed Hills Rural Artspace
CF71 7DP
www.coedhills.co.uk

The Courtyards
BA15 3PB

Coventry Peace House
CV6 5DS
www.covpeacehouse.org.uk

Earth Heart
DE6 1NS
www.earthheartcoop.co.uk

Edinburgh Student Housing Co-op
EH10 4HR
www.eshc.coop

Faslane Peace Camp
G84 8NT
faslanepeacecamp.wordpress.com

Findhorn Foundation
IV36 3TZ
www.findhorn.org

Firelight Housing Co-op
LS6 2JG

Frankleigh House
BA15 2PB

Giroscope
HU3 6BH
www.giroscope.co.uk

Glyn Abbey
SA15 5TL

Golem Housing Co-op
SA1 6AB
golemcoop.blogspot.co.uk

Gorsehill Housing Co-op
CH45 9JA

Green Wood Housing Co-op
LS8 4DW
https://greenwoodcoop.wixsite.com/
greenwoodhousingcoop

Grow Heathrow
UB7 0JH

Gung Ho Housing Co-op
B29 7PX
www.gungho.org.uk

Hammerhead Housing Co-op
BS5 7JE

Hamwic Housing Co-op
SO17 1WF
www.hamwichousingcoop.co.uk

Hargrave Road Community
N19 6SJ

Heartwood Community
SA17 5ES
www.heartwood.moonfruit.com

Hoathly Hill Community
RH19 4SJ
www.hoathlyhilltrust.org.uk

Iona Community
PA76 6SN
www.iona.org.uk

L'Arche Highlands
IV2 4QR
www.larchehighland.org.uk

L'Arche Ipswich
IP1 3QU
larcheipswich.org.uk

L'Arche London
SE27 9JU
www.larchelondon.org.uk

Lammas
SA34 0YD

The Land of Roots
DH7 8EN

Lee Abbey Aston
B6 5ND
leeabbeysmc.org/communities/aston-birmingham

Lee Abbey Knowle
BS4 1JN
leeabbeysmc.org/communities/knowle-west-bristol

Milltown Community
AB30 1PB
www.camphillscotland.org.uk/community/milltown

Monkton Wyld Court
DT6 6DQ
www.monktonwyldcourt.co.uk/

Mornington Grove Community
E3 4NS
www.morningtongrovecommunity.org.uk

New Ground Cohousing
N16 8WH
www.owch.org.uk

Newbold House
IV36 2RE
www.newboldtrust.org

Newton Dee Camphill Village
AB15 9DX
www.newtondee.org.uk

Oakfield Road Community
N4 4LB

Othona West Dorset
DT6 4RN
www.othonawestdorset.org.uk

Pengraig Community
SA44 5HS

People in Common
BB5 5UP

Permanent Housing Co-op
ST10 0BG

Pilsdon at Malling Community
ME19 6HH
www.pilsdonatmalling.org.uk

Plants For A Future
PL22 0QJ
www.pfaf.org

Ploughshare Housing Co-op
EH10 4JQ

Random Camel Housing Co-op
IP4 1BQ
randomcamelcoop.wordpress.com

Redcurrant Housing Co-op
G5 0HY
redcurranthousingcoop.wordpress.com

Rose Howey Housing Co-operative
L8
rosehowey.wordpress.com

Rubha Phoil Forest Garden
IV45 8RS
www.skye-permaculture.org.uk

Sahaja
SP3 5DJ

Scargill House
BD23 5HU
www.scargillmovement.org

Shrub Family
NR16 2QT

Stepping Stones Housing Co-op
NP25 4L
www.highburyfarm.org.uk

Stourbridge Camphill Houses
DY8 3YA
www.camphillvillagetrust.org.uk/locations/stourbridge

Summerhill Housing Co-op
NE4 6EB

Taliesin Housing Co-op
SY20 8JH

Tan-y-Fron Housing Co-op
SY22 6BP
tanyfronhousingco-op.weebly.com

Tangram Housing Co-op
LS8 5AD

West End Housing Co-op
NE4 5NL
www.westendhousingco-op.co.uk

Whiteway Colony
GL6 7EP

Wild Futures Monkey Sanctuary
PL13 1NZ
www.wildfutures.org

Windsor Hill Wood
BA4 4JE
www.windsorhillwood.co.uk

DEVELOPING COMMUNITIES

These listings represent a moment in time. As such, communities that were forming in the last directory may now be developing and well on their way to becoming established, others may be at an earlier stage in this process.

Angel Yard is in Norwich, a medieval city in the East of England, UK. Norwich is 90 minutes away from London by train and 30 minutes' drive from the nearest beach. Our two-thirds-of-an-acre site (approx. 0.27 hectares) is on Sussex Street, a Georgian and Victorian residential area close to the city centre. It used to be home to Sussex House but, following bomb damage, it became a mason's yard and then an industrial unit. The site is a short walk from the River Wensum and Marriott's Way, an off-road cycle and foot path. It's close to Magdalen Street, a vibrant area with a rich mix of independent shops and cafes. There's a zero-waste store, vegan and vegetarian-friendly restaurants, record and vintage shops, charity shops and supermarkets. Our first members came together in 2015 when we bought our main site, subsequently buying a plot of land next door at auction. Although the site originally had planning permission, we have decided to draw up a fresh application to bring the design up to date and reflect our wishes. Working with TOWN, developers of the award-winning Marmalade Lane cohousing community in Cambridge, we appointed Archio as our project architects in 2020.

Angel Yard Cohousing

Location
East Anglia

Electronic Mail
hello@angelyard.org.uk

World Wide Web *www.angelyard.org.uk*

Barney Fields Elders

Barney Fields is a development of new homes in Hartland, a picturesque village on North Devon's Atlantic coast. Plans are being developed to deliver sustainable homes designed with home-working in mind, spaces to grow food and a co-housing community for over 55s. These elements are to be set within an ecologically rich pedestrian-priority landscape where children can explore and play freely. Barney Fields Elders is an over 55s Co-housing community which will be located in a quiet and sunny corner of the wider Barney Fields development surrounded by native hedgerows within a short walk of the village centre. It will be a planned, small, elders' eco-cohousing community. The 13 houses and a common house are currently being designed by an architect, with input from prospective community members. The two-bedroom houses will all be for sale at an amount that will include a one-thirteenth share of the ownership of the common house.

Location
South West England

Electronic Mail
barneyfieldshartland@gmail.com

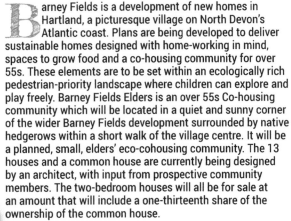

World Wide Web *www.barneyfields.co.uk/barney-fields-elders*

Chapeltown Cohousing

Chapeltown Cohousing is creating sustainable and affordable homes for 33 households. Transforming derelict land into a vibrant neighbourhood with low-energy homes, shared facilities and gardens, recreational space, opportunities for inter-generational connections and a diverse intentional community grown from the local area. What makes this venture special is that it is run by local people to benefit local people. At least two-thirds of the residents will come from Chapeltown. We are also working hard to make sure that the group reflects the diversity of the local area in terms of age, ethnicity and wealth.

Location
North of England

Electronic Mail
info@chapeltowncohousing.org.uk

World Wide Web *www.chapeltowncohousing.org.uk*

At the time of writing we are close to securing land in Cirencester near the town centre for our co-housing development of approximately 32 flats and houses, some for sale, some for rent. All buildings will be built to Passivhaus standard with access to a central area for safe play and community activities, gardens, allotments and a playground. Our common house is the jewel in the crown – an exciting design with a large hall, kitchen, creche, laundry, meeting and guest rooms.

Cirencester Cohousing

Location
South West England

Electronic Mail
enquiry@cirencoho.org.uk

World Wide Web *www.cirencoho.org.uk/*

Our core aims: Integration into Falmouth, not an alternative community; MHOS model of ownership; Close enough to walk and cycle to local amenities; Ecologically responsible method of construction and energy positive; Shared facilities- including laundry/workshop/garden and allotment/play; Priority on car sharing/electric vehicles; Economic incentive – a collective business: Community café? Maybe a repair shop? Or even holiday destination? People outside of Falmouth are welcome to join the group, but it will not be on a first come first served basis, instead prioritized for local people. Each household will be required to contribute some working capital or sweat equity at risk to secure their place as a member. This investment will enable the group to hire professional services to create a strong legal framework and enable future investment to secure land and construction costs. We have only just begun the adventure. The most important thing to remember is that is about building the community, even before we build. Hopefully after the process, which we like to think of as a dance rather than a journey, should give everyone a chance to know for certain that Ambos is for them. The group will periodically offer invites to the town until we have full membership.

Falmouth & Penryn Cohousing

Location
South West England

Electronic Mail
hello@ambos.org.uk

World Wide Web *www.ambos.org.uk*

Five Rivers Cohousing

Location
North of England

Electronic Mail
5riverscohousing2012@gmail.com

Set up in 2012, we have done a lot of background work and made many attempts at getting a site in Sheffield, from bidding at auction, to working with local housing associations, and so on. We had high hopes in late 2019 but that one also fell through when the developer pulled out. We did, though, get a grant from Homes England and have been benefitting greatly from the help of a professional Development Consultant. In early 2021, we are in renewed discussions with another developer about a site on the west side of the city. We are aiming for 10-25 units, of varying sizes and high-eco sustainable build, that are multi-affordable, and lived in by a multi-generational community. So we are very keen for more people to join us, to be part of developing our plans, and if possible to pledge some capital towards the costs.

World Wide Web *sheffieldcohonetwork.wordpress.com/current-groups*

Paradise Valley

Location
The Midlands

Electronic Mail
robin@om-shanti.org.uk

We own 22 acres of woodland and pasture near Bromyard in Herefordshire and are creating an ecological and personal growth community, living as self-sufficiently as we are able. We are off-grid. We are managing our woodland in accord with a Woodland Management Plan and, in the long run, will use timber from it and clay from the earth to build our low-impact dwellings. We have a planning consultant working with us and and already have permission for a round-wood timber framed barn for use in connection with our forestry activity and are cutting and preparing timber for this barn. We aim to be self-sufficient in food and are applying permacultural practices to achieve this. We are vegan, alcohol-free, tobacco-free and drug-free. We intend that participants will live and work on the land, with outside working only where absolutely necessary. We have formed the Living Land Trust, which will own the land and the buildings. We will work with Herefordshire Wildlife Trust to create a plan for protecting and enhancing the wildlife on our land. We are open to new participants who want to live and work on the land, and who are committed to their personal growth and to that of those they will be living with.

World Wide Web *www.paradisevalleycommunity.co.uk*

Shangrileeds is a small, emerging co-housing group based in Leeds. Our aim is to develop an urban, intergenerational cohousing community within Leeds. We aim to create 10 to 20 homes (from 1 bed flats up to 4 bed houses) and a "common-house" which will include features for residents such as laundry, shared kitchen and meeting space as well as offering facilities for the local community. We hope to have a low impact on the environment subject to financial constraints and be accessible to people on modest incomes. The group has developed a vision, policies, an initial business plan and is registered as a limited company. We work on Co-operative principles and consensus decision making. A legal body (probably a co-operative) will own the site/development and residents will own shares equivalent to the value of their own unit and contribute to the cost of the shared facilities. Over the years, we have actively bid for a number of sites in Leeds and have good links with the local Council and Leeds Community Homes who are working with us to pursue our project. We are always keen to recruit new, active members to help us shape and move the project on. We are looking for a diverse, inte -generational group of individuals who share our values and vision.

Shangrileeds

Location
North of England

Electronic Mail
shangrileeds@gmail.com

World Wide Web *shangrileeds.wordpress.com*

Still Green are moving to Wolverton! Planning permission for a larger development of which we will be a part was submitted in early December 2020. We are looking to move in during the later part of 2022. Twenty-nine 1 to 3-bed apartments, each with their own private outside area, and a shared 'common house' will surround a south-facing courtyard garden. We are working closely with the landscape consultant on the design for the garden and with a specialist accessibility consultant. Our homes will be built to high sustainability standards and benefit from being part of a scheme-wide community-owned energy system. Our 'common house' will be at the heart of the community and will have a south-facing kitchen, living and dining area for communal meals and events that will open out onto a large terrace, as well as a guest bedroom, shared laundry and bike/mobility scooter store. The wider Love Wolverton scheme is located within Wolverton Conservation Area and will regenerate the town centre, providing a mix of well-designed apartments and family houses as well as new shops, cafes and other amenities to reinstate the historic high street and commercial core of Wolverton. This is going to be a great location for a senior cohousing community.

Still Green

Location
South East England

Electronic Mail
stillgreenweb@gmail.com

World Wide Web *www. stillgreenweb.org*

OTHER FORMING COMMUNITIES

Setting up an intentional community can be a long and winding road which sees some lost along the way and others reborn or invigorated by changing times and membership. In an attempt to capture communities that are starting out or forming we have included some of the communities who have listings on the Diggers and Dreamers website, but have not updated their entry for some time.

Bridge Farm Bristol
South West England
www.bridgefarmbristol.co.uk

Bridport Cohousing
South West England
www.bridportcohousing.org.uk

Cardiff Cohousing
Wales
www.cardiff-cohousing.uk

Clachan Cohousing
Scotland
www.clachancohousing.co.uk

Coral Co-housing
South East England
www.coralcohousing.co.uk

Dandelion Community
South West England
www.dandelioncommunity.co.uk

Hazel Co-operative
South East England
www.hazelcoop.com

Hope Cohousing
Scotland
www.hopecohousing.org

Kent Cohousing
South East England
www.kentcohousing.co.uk

Lowfield Green Housing Co-op
North of England
www.yorspace.org

Nottingham Cohousing
The Midlands
www.nottinghamcohousing.org.uk

Ryedale Cohousing
North of England

Sorrel Housing Co-op
South West England
www.facebook.com/SorrelHousingCoop

Tortoiseshell Housing Co-op
Wales
www.cragencrwban.wordpress.com

Useful Books

Starting a Community

■ BAKER , B. *With a Little Help from Our Friends: Creating Community as We Grow Older.* Vanderbilt University Press; (2014) ISBN: 978-0826519887

■ BUNKER, S et al (eds). *Cohousing in Britain: A Diggers & Dreamers Review.* Diggers and Dreamers Publications (2011) ISBN: 978-0954575731

■ BUNKER, S et al (eds). *Low Impact Living Communities in Britain: A Diggers & Dreamers Review.* Diggers and Dreamers Publications (2014) ISBN: 978-0954575748

■ CHATTERTON, P. *Low Impact Living: A Field Guide to Ecological, Affordable Community Building.* Routledge (2014) ISBN: 978-0415661614

■ DURRETT, C. *The Senior Cohousing Handbook: A Community Approach to Independent Living.* New Society Publishers; (2nd edition 2009) ISBN-13: 978-0865716117

■ FIELD, M et al (eds). *The UKCN Practical Guide to Cohousing.* Diggers & Dreamers
Publications; (2022)
ISBN: to be confirmed

Sarah Eno is a former member of Parsonage Farm, Crabapple and Laurieston Hall. She was co-author of The Collective Housing Handbook and after many years of living in the world outside of intentional community she is convenor of the developing Vanilla Cohousing Community.

Reviewed by Sarah Eno

The Guide is distillation of the collective experience of many people and groups over many years. This is the first major handbook on cohousing for the UK and the authors, cohousing groups and the organisations are to be commended. With 172 pages, it is packed, truly packed with information, important issues to consider, key points, suggestions, tools, tips and links to other resources. Throughout it is enlivened by lovely sunny photographs and pertinent quotes from groups.

The Guide is indeed very practical as it focusses on the nuts and bolts of the journey. It is organised under five key development Phases: GROUP, SITE, PLAN, BUILD, LIVE with three additional information sections – DESIGN, FINANCE and RESOURCES. Early on, page 16 in fact, there is an excellent summary of these Phases and the Content which the Guide describes in detail on the pages under each Phase. These five Phases comprise a time sequence which a group will roughly follow but cohousing development is an iterative process so users will always be travelling both ways; always looking ahead for what needs thinking about; making decisions then going back to check information and options.

Colour coding is used throughout for each Phase - so GROUP is blue, SITE is pale green, BUILD is orange, DESIGN is grey and so on. The first two pages of each Phase comprise a list of key topics which will be addressed in sections on the following pages. The following sections are designed as a double page spreads, with the left page concentrating on matters to be considered under that topic and the opposite, right hand page headed Advice to Groups. The last pages of each Phase lists available support either from the Community Led Housing accredited Advisors or other stakeholders who might offer relevant help. Included throughout are numerous opportunities to click to web links, further details and other resources.

For example, in the Phase headed SITE, 'Identifying land or property' which is one of six key topics, the left page mentions a need for a group to be open to opportunities and discusses eight potential opportunities a group might consider, from brownfield to historic buildings. The opposite page includes advice such as drawing up a site assessment checklist, offers

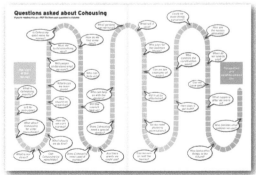

Questions asked about Cohousing

some group experiences, notes 'keep the planners sweet' and reminds us that most sites will not be perfect so be prepared to compromise.

The Resources section (paperclip icon tab) is a very good place to go to get a feel for what cohousing means, what is about and the differences with 'normal' housing, the challenges it and groups face, case studies of some well established cohousing groups, types of tenure and a list of books about cohousing and useful websites. It could be a good chapter to introduce new people to the concept.

I was initially dismayed that the information is so England based, but it was funded by Community Led Housing and UKCN. Page 158 covers the devolved nations all in one section, which is fair enough. To reach the same level of expertise is a substantial job for us in Scotland, but this Guide is a brilliant model to which to add our particular circumstances!

Lastly, while it is worth a group reading the whole Guide, it is so detailed it could be overwhelming. Being selective is an important task as different groups will need to pick up on different things; some aspects could perhaps be ignored; others will be key issues. A group could perhaps divide up the material as study topics or mini workshops and come together to discuss, note and list what is important to the group; what has to be done, what has been done and so on..... I would be tempted to print some specific summary pages to have in front of me, but the whole Guide is basically essential reading.

Sustaining the Community's Vision is one of the last topics to be discussed in the LIVE Phase, but this will be needed all the way through your journey. You will be ably assisted and inspired by this Guide to have a well informed trip!

■ JANZEN, D. *Intentional Christian Community Handbook.* Paraclete Press (2012) ISBN: 978-1612612379

■ LEAFE CHRISTIAN, D. *Creating a Life Together: Practical Tools to Grow Ecovillages and Intentional Communities.* New Society Publishers (2003) ISBN: 978-0865714717

■ LEAFE CHRISTIAN, D. *Finding Community: How to Join an Ecovillage or Intentional Community.* New Society Publishers (2007)
ISBN: 978-0865715783

■ McCAMANT, K and DURRETT, C. *Creating Cohousing: Building Sustainable Communities.* New Society Publishers, (2011)
ISBN: 978-0865716728

■ PLUHAR, A. *Sharing Housing: A Guidebook for Finding and Keeping Good Housemates.* Homemate Publishing; (2nd edition (2011)
ISBN: 978-0991010400

■ RADICAL ROUTES. *How to set up a Housing Co-op.* Radical Routes Publications

■ SEEDS FOR CHANGE. *A Consensus Handbook: Co-operative Decision Making for Activists, Co-ops and Communities.* Seeds for Change Lancaster Co-operative Ltd (2013)
ISBN: 978-0957587106

Individual UK Communities

■ COATES, C. *A Life in Common.* Diggers and Dreamers Publications (2021)
ISBN: 978-1838472504

■ HEART, M and WHITE, D. *Anarchists, Hippies and Other Undesirables: Alternative Living, Politics and Optimism 1972-1985.* CreateSpace Independent Publishing Platform (2015)
ISBN: 978-1512280005

■ JONES, T. *A Place of Refuge: An Experiment in Communal Living – The Story of Windsor Hill Wood.* Quercus (2015)
ISBN: 978-1848662483

JONES, T. *Utopian Dreams.* Faber & Faber (2008)
ISBN: 978-0571223817

MELTZER, G. *Findhorn Reflections: A very personal take on life inside the famous spiritual community and ecovillage.* CreateSpace Independent Publishing Platform (2015)
ISBN: 978-1512006513

REID, M. *Mix Café – Memoir of Laurieston Hall 1972-1977.* McConnell & Co (2019)
ISBN: 978-1527237605

ROWLANDS, R. *An Adventure Shared: The story of the first Quaker Community at Bamford.* Diggers and Dreamers Publications (2016)
ISBN: 978-0954575762

SAWTELL, R, *Under One Roof: The story of a Christian community.*
Darton, Longman & Todd Ltd (2015)
ISBN: 978-0232531732

Lucy Sargisson has reviewed both of the following books for us. She says: "They're a good read, telling compelling stories, offering lasting lessons and I hope they get widely read. Each book is about a significant intentional community, founded in the 1970s (and still existing) and each is told through the voices of multiple members. Here the similarity between the books ends. They are very different."

SPRECKLEY, F and SIMS, H. *Commune on the Moors: A Story of Lifespan.*
Diggers & Dreamers Publications (2020)
ISBN: 978-0954575786

Reviewed by Lucy Sargisson

Commune on the Moors: a story of Lifespan was carefully compiled and edited by founding members, Hylda Sims and Freer Spreckley. They sought to develop a community dedicated to a lifelong Summerhill-inspired learning. The book opens with a memorial for Hylda, who died in January 2020, just after completion of the final draft. Most of the content is chronologically structured, starting in 1974 with the negotiation of a bold deal with the local council and the owner of 19 former railway workers cottages on the edge of the South Yorkshire moors. It moves

through the community's formative years of property renovation, changes in the 80s, collapse in the 1990s, and its subsequent rescue and revival.

There is a lot of be learned from this history. All intentional communities are different but Lifespan's journey is a familiar one. The early days required commitment: life was physically tough, frugal and fully communal: sharing income and living together. Goodwill, collaboration, ingenuity and focus shine out from the accounts of these days. After a while, with major renovations achieved, frictions and factions emerged and things became messy. People left, people joined, the community changed. Conflict occurred over all of the things that cause conflict in intentional communities: personalities, relationships, structures and processes, values, community finances and the final conflict (over the ownership of the property) led to its abandonment in the mid 90s. It was resurrected by a tribe of road protestors. Current members live with looser ties than the founding group, mostly in separate flats or houses, although the community kitchen and recreation room are still used. As a story of the rise, fall and rise again of Lifespan, Commune on the Moors is instructive. Hylda and Freer have gathered together accounts from former and current members, drawn on key documents and archives, such as Lifespan Community Diary, leaflets and publications, so that the book genuinely seems to combine many voices into one story. It's meticulously done and it must have taken a long time.

If this were the only contribution made by the book, it would be valuable. Other groups can learn from these experiences, so carefully told. However, the book offers much more than this. Several of the chapters offer 'wider' lessons drawn deeply from experience; lessons about housing, work, sharing, economics, education and living lightly. The Foreword makes three proposals:

1. Encourage councils to find and support community/cohousing/ co-op/self-build housing projects as a version of council housing.

2. Encourage the participation of prospective tenants in hands-on designing, renovating, managing and maintaining these projects.

3. Be prepared to compulsorily purchase land, requisition unoccupied dwellings and decriminalise squatting (p9-10).'

4. There are many more lessons and it's worth reading the book to discover them.

Lucy Sargisson is Professor Emeritus of Utopian Studies (University of Nottingham). She has published several books and articles about intentional communities in New Zealand and the UK and has just discovered the beauty of dancing Five Rhythms on a hilltop while the sun goes down over the sea.

■ TREANOR, D et al. *Anatomy of a Commune: Laurieston Hall 1972-1987*. Diggers & Dreamers Publications (2021)
ISBN: 978-0954575793

Reviewed by Lucy Sargisson

Anatomy of a Commune consists of thirtyseven mostly single-authored chapters. Some people have written one chapter, some more than one. The overall structure is chronological, starting with 'How it all began' and ending with `New Beginnings'. But the chapters don't quite match their titles. Well, they do, but not in a conventional way – and perhaps that's appropriate for the community. For example, I expected 'How it all began' to talk about things like the founders' shared beliefs, why they wanted to start a new community, how they raised the funds and acquired the property. And there are glimpses of some of these things, but that's not what the chapter is about. Instead, it's about the author: her conflicted/conflictual history in feminist activism, her intimate relationships, her desire for a more feminist and better way of life. It's a fascinating read – indeed, each of the chapters is a fascinating read.

But it's not quite what I expected. This is not a criticism – I love the way this book disrupts expectations, resisting a simple coherent narrative. It's one of the most interesting community memoirs I've read. It will present a challenge to people who want to know 'the history' of Laurieston Hall because it is, as the title suggests, an 'anatomy'. It's an examination of the parts that make up the whole.

The book gains coherence from the work of its four editors. There's a timeline of key moments from 1972-87, which lists things like the establishment of the People Centre and Freefall project and the beginning of the Exodus. As an outsider, it was hard to get a sense of the importance of these events until reading each chapter and realising that they crop up, over and again. Then the triumph of, for example, finishing the Aga kitchen and the trauma of the Exodus came to life. Each of the contributors is introduced at the beginning of the book and the editors also offer brief introductions at the beginning of each chapter. These are helpful, providing some context about each contributor. What the book doesn't have is an overarching narrator binding the parts together, giving the reader a 'big picture'.

The chapters vary greatly in style and content. Some (a minority) are analytical. Most are very personal. Some are poetic. Some contain thoughts that stream onto the page. Many draw on individual diaries and almost all articulate their author's feelings. Indeed, feelings and emotions cry out from the pages of this book. It's an emotionally generous work, in which the contributors share some of the joys and a lot of the deep pain of a radical experiment in alternative living. It is a touching testament to the highs and lows of combining the personal and the political in daily life. Risk and trust are big themes. For example, members took huge *risks to their emotional and mental health (e.g. 'criticism meetings', self-help therapy, open relationships, structurelessness) and these required a lot of trust.*

As with Lifespan, Laurieston Hall experienced periods when things went well and periods when the community energy lashed inwards - destructive and lacerating. And the causes of conflict were similar, although the one that screams from the page in many of the chapters is pain around relationships. Desire and love and rejection and jealousy and loneliness can break your heart. But members also speak of resilience and of the power of making things happen, creating better ways of doing things (e.g. meetings, communication, living authentically, generating income). It's a long list and these are just examples. The books contains many more insights and it's worth reading it to discover them.

▇ VINCENT, J (ed). *Christian Communities.* Ashram Press (2011) ISBN: 978-0955907326

▇ WIMBUSH, P. *The Birth of an Ecovillage.* FeedaRead.com (2012) ISBN: 978-1781764923

▇ WIMBUSH, P. *The Lammas Ecovillage* . FeedaRead.com (2021) ISBN: 9781839457869

Communal History

▇ BARLOW, K. *The Abode of Love: The Remarkable Tale of Growing Up in a Religious Cult.* Mainstream Publishing (2007), ISBN: 978-1845962135

▇ COATES, C. *Utopia Britannica: British Utopian Experiments 1325 – 1945.* Diggers & Dreamers Publications (2001), ISBN: 978-0951494585

▇ COATES, C. *Communes Britannica: A History of Communal Living in Britain: 1939 – 2000* . Diggers & Dreamers Publications (2013), ISBN: 978-0951494592

■ WORPOLE, K. *No matter how many skies have fallen.* Liitle Toller Books (2021)
ISBN: 978-1908213860

Reviewed by Kirsten Stevens-Wood

It is often said that intentional communities are formed from the dissatisfaction of the society and times from which they are born. Ken Worpole's book is an excellent example of this, set between two devastating wars, he describes a community which is formed at a time when the ravages of the first world war were still creating shadows over the population of England with many of the community members having direct or close family experiences of the horrors of the first world war as unrest begins to stir once again. Within this context Worpole weaves together the story of an eclectic group of utopians, pacifists and conscientious objectors who come together to collectively purchase Frating Hall Farm, near Colchester. Their vision is that of a socialist, Christian back to the land community providing in part refuge and farm work to those who chose not to or could not go to war. Fascinatingly, Frating Hall Farm is less than 12 miles from the contemporary community of Old Hall although they were separated by almost 20 years.

As a book it works well in creating the feel of the time, different social mores, for example only married couples being allowed to live together, and the backdrop of food scarcity and rationing. The photographs are evocative of a time now past and beautifully capture the period with the men at work on the land in shirts, women with their hair curled in the styles of the time and harvest festival celebrations. Interestingly, there are also similarities to many modern-day communities for example, communal meals, shared projects, activism and also pinch points around things like childcare and the allocation of accommodation or resources. Frating Hall Farm only existed as a community for eleven years between 1943 and 1954, however, from the letters, documents and spoken history that Worpole has managed to piece together, it was an influential time for all involved and particularly warmly remembered by the (now adult) children as an idyllic time of immense freedom and a wonderful place to grow up. At its dissolution, the farm was taken on by the son of one of the community members who continues to farm the land to the present day.

No matter how many skies have fallen
Back to the land in wartime Britain

Ken Worpole

Another aspect of the book is its links to the literary giants of the time, including D.H Lawrence (from who's writing the title is derived), George Orwell and the famous writer and pacifist Vera Brittain. It seems that many of the great writers and thinkers of the time were keen to dip their toes into communal living although none of them actually joined the community. In some ways, this is a book that leaves you wanting more, it is a patchwork of accounts which can only partially create the whole picture of what it was like to have lived in those extraordinary times. Hopefully Ken Worpole will extend his research of this and other historical communities so that we may know more.

Useful Websites

Camphill England and Wales
www.camphill.org.uk

Foundation for Intentional Community
www.ic.org

Camphill Northern Ireland
www.camphillni.org

Gaia Eco-villages Network
www.gaia.org

Camphill Scotland
www.camphillscotland.org.uk

Intentional Communities Desk
www.communa.org.il

Camphill Village Trust
www.camphillvillagetrust.org.uk

International Communal Studies Ass.
www.communa.org.il/icsa

Confederation of Co-op Housing
www.cch.coop

LowImpact.org
www.lowimpact.org

Co-op and Community Finance
www.coopfinance.coop

One Planet Council
www.oneplanetcouncil.org.uk

Co-operatives UK
www.uk.coop

Permaculture Association
www.permaculture.org.uk

Ecology Building Society
www.ecology.co.uk

Permanent Publications
www.permaculture.co.uk

Eurotopia
www.eurotopia.directory

Radical Routes
www.radicalroutes.org.uk

■ Rootstock
www.rootstock.org.uk

■ Rhizome
www.rhizome.coop

■ Students for Co-operation
www.students.coop

■ This Land is Ours
www.tlio.org.uk

■ Triodos Bank
www.triodos.co.uk

■ UK Cohousing Network
www.cohousing.org.uk

■ Workaway
www.workaway.info

■ World Wide Opportunities on Organic Farms
www.wwoof.org.uk

The Diggers & Dreamers Reviews

Cohousing in Britain
Sarah Bunker et al (eds)
163 pp £12, ISBN: 978-0-9545757-3-1

*A look at how the cohousing
movement is developing in Britain*

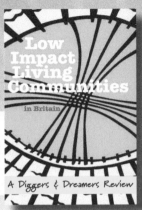

Low Impact Living Communities in Britain
Sarah Bunker et al (eds)
152 pp £12, ISBN: 978-0-9545757-4-8

Focus on off-grid communities.

Historical Books from D&D

Utopia Britannica
Chris Coates
312 pp £16.50, 978-0-9514945-8-5

*British utopian experiments
from 1325 to 1945*

Communes Britannica
Chris Coates
520 pp £25, ISBN: 978-0-9514945-9-2

*A history of communal living in Britain
from 1939 to 2000*

Communal Histories from D&D

An Adventure Shared

Rachel Rowlands
198 pp £12, ISBN: 978-0-9545757-6-2

*The story of the first Quaker
Community at Bamford*

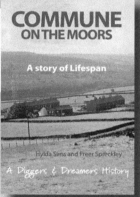

Commune on the Moors

Freer Spreckley and Hylda Sims
200 pp £12, ISBN: 978-0-9545757-8-6

*A history of the Lifespan Community –
high up in the Pennines*

Anatomy of a Commune

Dave Treanor et al (eds)
358 pp £12, ISBN: 978-0-9545757-9-3

*Multiple perspectives on the first 15
years of Laurieston Hall Community*

A LIfe in Common

Chris Coates
198 pp £12, ISBN: 978-1-8384725-0-4

*Recollections of People in Common –
from Burnley to Altham Corn Mill*

The Editors

James Dennis, born 1980, has spent the last six and a half years since the last edition living and working manual jobs in about equal measure between Scotland, England and Wales. He's managed to cut it about equal since the last edition. Still a vagrant and still moving about between communities. He has successfully survived 41 years in his current state of being and is backing robot overlords to bail us all out. He still likes Jung. He's been loved and rejected, heartbroken and joyous, he's been arrested and charged and fired and hired... the big surprise is he's not quit any jobs or relationships, so must congratulate himself on that score.

Chris Coates, born 1957. He has a sort of coun| cultural CV that is intertwined with the more normal | of his life. So while his job applications say that | been an actor, stage manager, building site labou| carpenter, construction project manager and caretake his AltCV might read: squatter, street performer, clo road protestor, peace activist, communard, co-opera father, tree planter, anarchist, author, Enginee the Imagination, 'President' of the Internati Communal Studies Association, Green F Councillor, cohousing pioneer.

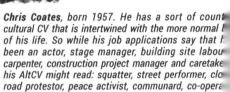

Kirsten Stevens-Wood, born 1972, joined the D&D collective in 2019. She is a senior lecturer for Cardiff Metropolitan University and leads the Intentional Communities Research Group which hosts the bi-annual Intentional Communities Symposium: a collection of research presentations, talks and workshops, usually on a theme. Outside of this Kirsten is a keen but chaotic gardener, beekeeper and woodswoman who resides permanently on the edge of all things interesting. Kirsten is an ethnographic researcher and relentlessly exploits this to spend as much time away from the office visiting as many different types of communities as possible.

Jonathan How, born 1953. Desi| co-operator, data manager and g| mayor. Now has half a century unde| belt of thinking that the world is going t| in a handcart. Tries to use his skills to alternative ideas jump the chasm and becom new normal. Wants to dispel the "right-brain: good brain: bad" myth that pervades contrarian thinking - right-brain balance being the important thing. A m of Redfield Community from 1984-96. "Communal may not be for everyone but intentional communities well become 'islands of coherence' in a world – just a the corner – where energy is no longer cheap!"